A magnificent job! This is a great book, loaded with what people need to know.
Debbie Clyne
Emergency Co-ordinator, City of Burnaby

This superb book could save your and your family's lives. One day a major earthquake in BC is certain to happen and nothing will be the same again.
Alex Tilley
Founder of Tilley Endurables Inc.

Wonderful resource for anyone living where earthquakes occur. Full of information! I learned so much from this material.
Jill Giel
National Director, Emergency Animal Rescue Service

Excellent, indispensible emergency guide. A must read before the Big One hits.
Bryan S. Shapiro
Partner, Shapiro Hankinson & Knutson

Having been in the emergency preparedness field for many years, I have read numerous guides and documents on the subject. Here, at last, is a book worth reading. It provides the widest range of options for surviving and moving on from the disaster looming over British Columbia — the inevitability of a Big One
J.- F. Landry
Principal and General Manager,
ER-Plus Risk Management Group Inc.

Reading this inspiring guide could be anyone's best chance for surviving the unthinkable.
Rob Southcott
Vancouver paramedic

Public awareness and public education are the keys to risk reduction. Being informed is a major part of being prepared and this guide does an admirable job.
Dr Hans Schreier
Professor of Agricultural Sciences Faculty,
University of British Columbia

It is your responsibility to be prepared. This excellent guide will help you and your family prepare for the Big One.
Greg Bennett
Emergency Planning Manager, BC Gas Utility Ltd

This manual is accurate and comprehensive. Following its guidelines might make the difference for you and your family between surviving and being a statistic.
Ed Frazer
Telecommunications engineer

EARTHQUAKE!

Preparing for the Big One

BRITISH COLUMBIA

EARTHQUAKE!
Preparing for the Big One

BRITISH COLUMBIA

Graem Castell

Pacific Rim Earthquake Preparedness Program Ltd
Vancouver, British Columbia, Canada

EARTHQUAKE! Preparing for the Big One
BRITISH COLUMBIA

Published by
Pacific Rim Earthquake Preparedness Program Ltd
PO Box 29193, 1950 West Broadway
Vancouver BC V6J 5C2
Canada

Editors: Tashon Ziara and Cathy Brannen
Proofreader: Deborah Wright
Cover design: Graem Castell and Ken White
Text design: Graem Castell and Ken White
Desktop publishing: U&I Type, Vancouver BC
"Knitting Sheep" by Tony Blundell, copyright Gallery Five Ltd, London
Map and diagrams: reproduced by Hale Yin and Vivian Liu
Screened photographs: reproduced with kind permission of the Office of Critical Infrastructure
Protection and Emergency Preparedness and the United States Geological Survey

First published 2002

Printed and bound in Canada by Friesens, Altona MB

National Library of Canada Cataloguing in Publication

Castell, Graem, 1939 -
Earthquake! preparing for the big one : British Columbia / Graem Castell.

Includes bibliographical references and index.
ISBN 0-9731829-0-3

1. Earthquakes—British Columbia. 2. Survival skills—British Columbia. 3.
Emergency management—British Columbia I. Pacific Rim Earthquake
Preparedness Program. II. Title.
HV551.5.C3C37 2002   613.6/9   C2002-911223-0

Efforts have been made to locate copyright holders of source material wherever possible.
The publisher welcomes hearing from any copyright holders of material used in this book
who have not been contacted and acknowledged.

DISCLAIMER
While the information and advice given in this book is believed to be accurate, no suggestions,
recommendations, or advice can be suitable for, or relevant to, every individual or circumstance.
The author and the publisher make no representations or warranties with respect to the accuracy or
completeness of the contents of this book and they disclaim any liability or loss of whatever nature
resulting from the use or misuse of the information and advice contained herein.

To

Alma Harvey
1924 - 2000

The most supportive
of mother-in-laws

ACKNOWLEDGEMENTS

The material in this book has been gathered from numerous sources. Some of these sources are acknowledged in the text and others, inevitably, are not. To all of those who have contributed to the wealth of earthquake and disaster preparedness knowledge and literature and those who play prominent roles in this field, I offer my heartfelt appreciation. In particular, I wish to thank the following — and many others whose names could not be included — for their willingness to answer my questions and contribute their expertise:

Frank Astorino
President,
John Fleming Insurance Agency Ltd

Greg Bennett
Emergency Planning Manager,
BC Gas Utility Ltd

Dr John Blatherwick
Chief Medical Health Officer,
Vancouver Coastal Health Authority

Scott Blessin
Operations Manager, Sensor Security Ltd

Leesa D. Bruce
Senior Director, Publications, Canadian
Pharmacists Association

Larry Campbell
former Chief Coroner of BC

Debbie Clyne
Emergency Co-ordinator, City of Burnaby

Ralph Currie
Subdivision Head, Geological Survey of
Canada, Pacific Division

Professor Lori Dengler
Director of the Humboldt Earthquake
Education Center, Humboldt State
University, Arcata, California

Ed Faust
Director of Product Management and
Business Development, Kidde plc

Sheila Fillman
Personal Lines Supervisor,
Pat Anderson Agencies

Ed Frazer
E. J. Frazer & Associates Ltd, Telecommunications Engineering Consultants

Carmen Funk
General Manager, First Aid & Survival
Technologies Limited

Robin Gardner
Corporate Security and Regional Emergency
Management Co-ordinator, GVRD

Jill Giel
National Director,
Emergency Animal Rescue Service

Brian Grant
Manager, Geoscience Initiatives,
British Columbia Geological Survey

Carrie Greschner
President,
Custom First Aid, Safety and Medical Inc.

David Gronbeck-Jones
Emergency Management Analyst
(Earthquakes),
Provincial Emergency Program

Peter Hadfield
Author of *Sixty Seconds that will Change the
World: the Coming Tokyo Earthquake*,
freelance journalist, and correspondent for
the CBC in Japan

Brian Inglis
Task Force Leader,
Vancouver Urban Search & Rescue

Ken Jones and John O'Sullivan
Operations Officers, QuakeKoso Canada Inc.

Jean-Francois Landry
Principal and General Manager,
ER-Plus Risk Management Group Inc.

Bryan Larrabee
Co-ordinator, Emergency Social Services,
City of Vancouver

Professors Simon LeVay and Kerry Sieh
Co-authors of *The Earth in Turmoil:
Earthquakes, Volcanoes,
and their Impact on Humankind*

Jay Lewis
President,
Terra Firm Earthquake Preparedness Inc.

Heather Lyle
Program Co-ordinator,
Emergency Management Division,
The Justice Institute of BC

Yan Michaud
Office of Critical Infrastructure Protection
and Emergency Preparedness

Craig Naherniak
General Manager,
Humane Education, BC SPCA

Andreas Nieman
Manager, Braidner Survival Kits Ltd

Lindsay Olson
Vice-President, Pacific Region,
Insurance Bureau of Canada

Jasmeen Panesar
Microbiologist and Quality Assurance
Manager, Canadian Springs Water Co

Lieutenant John Pye
Emergency Preparedness Division,
Vancouver Fire & Rescue Services

Bill Reid
President,
Reid Brothers Plumbing and Heating Ltd

Dr Hans Schreier
Professor of Agricultural Sciences Faculty,
Institute for Resources and Environment,
University of British Columbia

Mark Seemann
Emergency Management Analyst
for Seismic Hazards,
Provincial Emergency Program

Peter Severin
Manager, Consumer Relations, Sunbeam
Corporation (Canada) Limited

Tej Sidhu
Policy and Research Analyst,
Office of the Chief Coroner of BC

Rob Simpson
Principal,
Glotman Simpson Consulting Engineers

Rob Southcott
Vancouver paramedic

Jody Sydor
Director,
North Shore Emergency Management Office

Bruce Thompson
Emergency Planning Officer,
Thrifty Foods

Vivienne Taylor
Manager, Marketing and Communications,
Canada Mortgage & Housing Corporation

Alex Tilley
Founder, Tilley Endurables Inc.

Anne Ward
President, Krasicki & Ward Emergency
Preparedness Ltd

Randy Wolsey
Fire Chief, Edmonton AB: former Director of
Fire & Emergency Services, Delta BC

Daniel Wood
Vancouver writer

In addition, I should like to thank the team involved in the production of this book for their professionalism and helpfulness, and the many others whose feedback and suggestions have contributed to the usefulness of this guide.

EXPLANATIONS

This guide has received pre-publication acclaim from many quarters, including from supportive figures in government seismic circles who are not permitted to give private sector testimonials. It has also attracted pre-publication criticism (kindly put, because they like the guide as a whole) from a couple of respected academics for being too sensationalistic; for emphasizing the Big One (a Cascadia subduction zone megathrust earthquake) over other types of earthquake that may prove more critical for the province; for generalizing the likely damage to the region, when damage distribution will vary considerably; and for ignoring recent studies that indicate that people are more likely to prepare for an earthquake if the threat is presented in gentler terms.

I want you to be aware of this, but not to feel let off the hook. A catastrophic earthquake will be just that — catastrophic for many of us — and I don't want to write about it in subdued terms. If you're here when it happens and you get off lightly, I'm sure you'll be grateful. You will, however, be living in a devastated region for a long time to come and will be extremely grateful for the precautions you took head of time. And at some point we may debate whether I should have placed different emphases on the hazards we face and whether I should have couched them in less dramatic terms. Meanwhile, read on. I hope that this easily read, enjoyable guide will jolt you as well as lead you into whatever action may be needed.

On another note: throughout this book I have chosen to use the singular in the numerous situations where the plural might also apply. For example, while knowing that many households have more than one sleeping bag, I have put "_____ x sleeping bag" in various checklists, rather than "_____ x sleeping bag(s)." I have done this because, once started on the optional plural route, clumsy situations start turning up — for example, "your child(ren)'s school(s)," or "your pet's (or pets') harness(es)." Somewhat reluctantly, I have settled for "your child's school" and "your pet's harness," knowing that you may have six children, two dogs, and a baby crocodile to accommodate.

CONTENTS

Be resourceful!

OVERVIEW

As THIS PLANET HURTLES THROUGH SPACE, its surface plastered with our little empires, we can count ourselves fortunate that its molten outer core is as contained as it is by its far-from-leakproof crust. But just as a rhinoceros dislodges with a sudden shrug the white cattle egrets that perch symbiotically on its back, the Earth has regularly dislodged us. Recent earthquakes in Turkey, Taiwan, Japan, India, El Salvador, Afghanistan, and Iran, and thousands of years of seismic history, are testimony to that.

The last gigantic earthquake off the coasts of British Columbia and Washington occurred on January 26, 1700.[1] It is estimated as having been around 9.0 on the moment magnitude scale — about one hundred times more severe than the February 28, 2001 quake centred near Olympia, Washington. There were very few people here at that time — just a few First Nation settlements in a wilderness of trees. The region is now densely populated and contains just about everything that we need for our survival.

Big Ones have occurred in this part of the world at intervals of as few as 200 and as many as 800 years. The average interval has been in the region of 500 years.[2] "Great!" you might say. "So it could be a couple of hundred years before the next." It could be, indeed. Or it could be 20 minutes. As David Gronbeck-Jones, emergency management analyst (earthquakes) at the Victoria headquarters of the Provincial Emergency Program, points out, "Earthquakes don't happen according to averages."

Statistically, your home might be burgled once every 50 years and burn down once every 200 years but, if you are wise and can afford it, you insure against these threats now. Earthquake preparedness is just another form of insurance, and the next Big One could happen at any time.[3]

CRACKS IN THE SHELL

Under the soles of our feet and beneath all the oceans of the world, vast tectonic plates make up the crust of the Earth. Some of these are the size of continents; others are just a few hundred kilometres across. Typically, they are about 100 kilometres (60 miles) thick but, at certain points in the oceans, they are as thin as 8 kilometres (5 miles) and under parts of the continents, they are as much as 200 kilometres (120 miles) thick.[4] They contain, with considerable success, the molten core of this planet. If the earth were the size of an egg, its crust would be about the thickness of an eggshell.

These plates move under, over, or against each other, or sideways past each other, at rates of between 2.5 centimetres (1 inch) and 10 centimetres (4 inches) a year[5] — on average, at about the same rate that a fingernail grows. Miniscule though these movements may seem, they create enormous friction and it is the release of pent-up pressure within a plate, or where plates interface, that causes the violent shaking of an earthquake.

Four tectonic plates interact off the coast of British Columbia (*see diagram opposite*). About 500 kilometres (300 miles) southwest of Vancouver Island, the Juan de Fuca plate and the Pacific plate are diverging along the Juan de Fuca ridge. Much closer to Vancouver Island and extending all the way to Northern California, the Juan de Fuca plate converges with, and is sliding beneath, the North American plate on which Canada and the United States rest. Another, much smaller plate, the Explorer, is simultaneously sliding under the North American plate and past the Juan de Fuca plate. And, north of Vancouver Island and west of the Queen Charlotte Islands, the Pacific plate and North American plate are sliding past each other. It's a congested area!

THE RICHTER SCALE: Developed in 1935, and now of limited use, this is the most widely recognized measure of an earthquake's magnitude. It is logarithmic; each one-point increase on the scale represents a massive tenfold increase in the back-and-forth and up-and-down movement of the earth and thirty-two fold increase in the amount of energy released. An earthquake of magnitude 7.0 is major: it can cause immense damage and considerable loss of life. Imagine, then, one ten times more severe and thirty-two times more powerful at magnitude 8.0. And if that isn't daunting enough, imagine a magnitude 9.0 — 100 times more severe and 1,024 times more powerful than a magnitude 7.0. Another way of looking at it is that you would need more than a thousand magnitude 7.0 earthquakes occurring simultaneously to equal the magnitude of a 9.0 earthquake. It is sobering stuff.

THE MOMENT MAGNITUDE SCALE: Since the mid-1970s, seismologists have used the rather more sensitive moment magnitude scale to measure moderate to large earthquakes. Each unit on the scale represents a thirty-two fold increase in the total energy released in the earthquake. The moment magnitude and Richter scales are about the same for earthquakes up to a magnitude of 7.0, but the Chile earthquake of May 22, 1960 measured 8.5 on the Richter scale and 9.5 on the moment magnitude scale.

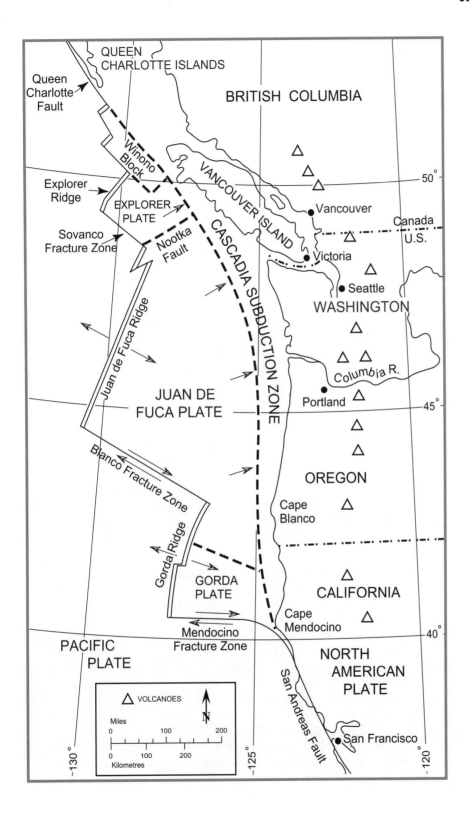

QUEEN
CHARLOTTE ISLANDS

BRITISH COLUMBIA

Queen
Charlotte
Fault

Winona
Block

VANCOUVER ISLAND

50°

Vancouver

Canada
U.S.

Explorer
Ridge

EXPLORER
PLATE

Sovanco
Fracture Zone

Nootka
Fault

CASCADIA SUBDUCTION ZONE

Victoria

Seattle

WASHINGTON

Juan de Fuca Ridge

JUAN DE
FUCA PLATE

Columbia R.

Portland

45°

OREGON

Blanco Fracture Zone

Cape
Blanco

Gorda Ridge

GORDA
PLATE

CALIFORNIA

Cape
Mendocino

Mendocino
Fracture Zone

40°

PACIFIC
PLATE

NORTH
AMERICAN
PLATE

San Andreas Fault

△ VOLCANOES

N

Miles
0   100   200

0   100   200
Kilometres

San Francisco

−130°

−125°

−120°

The earthquakes on this coast during the last 125 years, the brief period for which we have records, have been short duration, crustal quakes occurring within the Pacific, Juan de Fuca, Explorer, and North American plates. They happen to have been relatively minor, but a major quake within the Juan de Fuca or North American plates has the potential to inflict massive damage — because of its proximity to urban areas.

The quake that should perhaps most concern us, however — the monster quake, the next Big One — will occur not within the Juan de Fuca and North American plates, but where these plates interface.

MEGATHRUST QUAKES The interface between a subducting plate (such as the Juan de Fuca) and an overriding one (such as the North American) is known as a megathrust fault, and the earthquake caused by sudden slippage along such a fault is known as a megathrust quake. All of the world's largest earthquakes have been megathrust quakes.

There is evidence that the Juan de Fuca and North American plates are locked along their 1,200-kilometre (750-mile) interface. The pressure is building. If the whole of this locked area of nearly 100,000 square kilometres (30,000 square miles) — the Cascadia subduction zone — ruptures at once, the resulting earthquake is likely to be a truly giant one.[6]

In *The Earth in Turmoil: Earthquakes, Volcanoes, and their Impact on Humankind* (*see Section 30, Useful Reading*), Professor Kerry Sieh and Professor Simon LeVay put it this way. They use the moment magnitude scale:

> If the [Cascadia] subduction zone breaks as separate segments, each earthquake will probably have a magnitude of about 8.0. Geologist George Carver, of California State University, Humboldt, has called this the "decade of terror" scenario. Each event might well release at least 30 times more seismic energy than the 1995 earthquake that devastated Kobe, Japan, over a region several times larger.
>
> If the entire subduction zone breaks at once, the resulting earthquake would probably have a magnitude of about 9.0 — about a thousandfold more energetic than the Kobe quake, putting it on a par with the 1960 Chilean earthquake. The present evidence is too fragmentary to be sure which of these two scenarios will happen. It does seem probable, however, that at least the most recent of the previous earthquakes on the Cascadia subduction zone [January 26, 1700] involved a single rupture of the entire zone....
>
> The biggest earthquake ever recorded on Earth, the 1960 Chilean earthquake, produced by rupture of a 600-mile long segment of a subduction zone, had a magnitude of 9.5. The 1700 Cascadia subduction earthquake, as estimated from the Japanese tsunami records, had a magnitude of about 9.0.[7]

At 5:46 a.m. on January 17, 1995, a 20-second earthquake measuring 6.9 on the moment magnitude scale and 7.2 on the Richter scale, hit Kobe, Japan. Kobe, with a population of around 1.5 million, is similar in size to Greater Vancouver and, like Vancouver, it is a pivotal port city.

The Great Hanshin earthquake, as it was subsequently named, killed between 4,570 and 6,400 people (depending on which figures you believe) and injured 35,000 others. The earthquake and resulting fires — sections of the city were ablaze for days — badly damaged or destroyed 150,000 to 180,000 buildings, leaving 300,000 people homeless (237,000 people were in shelters on one peak day). Economic losses amounted to $300 billion US. Had that quake occurred while people were at work and on the streets and while children were at school, the number of people killed and seriously injured would have been much higher.

In BC, our casualties and economic losses may equal or exceed those sustained by the people of Kobe, if only because our earthquake could dwarf theirs. It is certain that there will be numerous deaths, countless injuries, massive destruction, and incalculable suffering. Many of our homes will collapse (*see Section 2, During the Big One*) and thousands of others will be uninhabitable. Virtually every home in the region will be damaged to some extent. In some areas, uncontrolled fires will erase forever what might have been recoverable.

Workplaces will be similarly hit. Many businesses will be wiped out, leaving owners and employees to ponder their newfound freedom. Lifestyles and futures will be wrecked in a matter of seconds. Schools, hospitals, and public buildings will be severely damaged; many will be closed, some indefinitely. Gas, hydro, water, sewage, and telephone lines will be broken or badly disrupted, wiping out means of heating, lighting, cooking, power, sanitation, hygiene, and communication.

In an instant, streets will become impassable, clogged with debris and stuck vehicles. Bridges and overpasses will be unusable. Much of our public transit system will be at a standstill. Supermarkets and corner stores will be cleared of food and useful items. There will be looting. For many of us, it will seem as if life will never be the same again — and, for many of us, it won't be.

These consequences of the quake are inevitable, but for those who have taken precautions, they will be largely manageable.

These pages are packed with information. In them you will find just about everything that anyone living in this earthquake zone should know, consider, or do in order to prepare for the quake that is bound to happen.

Section 1 stresses the importance of preparation — how vital it will be to have done your homework ahead of time.

Sections 2 and 3 outline what to expect, what to do, and what not to do, during the quake and its immediate aftermath.

Sections 4 and 5 cover the crucial subjects of water and food. Water lines will be severely damaged and almost all sources of water will be either obviously contaminated or suspect. Food store shelves will be cleared within minutes of a major quake. Having adequate reserves of drinkable water and suitable food — in the right locations — will be critical.

Section 6 looks at emergency methods of cooking, and Sections 7 and 8 describe alternative means of lighting, heating, and warmth, stressing the importance of having access to warm clothing whenever away from home — even in mid summer.

Sections 9 and 10 address emergency sanitation, toiletries, and medications, providing, for example, instructions for creating a Camosun commode (a makeshift toilet) using kitchen bags and duct tape.

There will be essential repairs to be made after the quake, and Section 11 deals with tools. The extent of the repairs will depend, in part, on how well your home, its contents, and its immediate surroundings were secured, so Section 12 offers suggestions and instructions for securing your home.

There's no telling where you'll be when the Big One hits, or whether you'll be able to leave or forced to stay there. You may be at work and unable to leave until the following morning. Your well-equipped vehicle may be unable to move because of blocked streets. Your well-stocked home may have partially collapsed, or be ablaze. Sections 13, 14, and 15, on workplaces, vehicles, and grab-and-go bags, prepare you for these eventualities.

People will be killed and injured in the Big One. Section 16 deals with emergency scene management, triage, trauma, and shock, and suggests appropriate contents for first aid kits. And Sections 17, 18, 19, and 20 describe the insidious but avoidable risks of hypothermia, fire, carbon monoxide poisoning, and natural gas explosions.

If you have pets, Section 21 covers just about everything that you will need to consider and do.

Almost the first thing that everybody in the stricken area will want to do is pick up a telephone and dial out — for help or to be in touch with loved ones. As the rest of the world hears of the quake, literally millions of people will attempt to call into the devastated area. Our networks will be swamped. Telephone calls in the aftermath of the Big One, along with other means of communication, are the subject of Section 22.

Many aspects of documentation are covered in Section 23. Section 24 covers the vital subject of insurance. And in Section 25 you will find a number of smart tips.

School emergency plans vary widely in British Columbia. Section 26 looks at the kinds of questions a parent should be asking of daycare centres, schools, and colleges.

Some of your emergency stocks — everything from batteries to food — will have to be regularly checked and updated. Section 27 covers these monthly, quarterly, semi-annual, and annual check-ups.

Sections 28 contains various warnings, and Section 29 looks at the wider picture — your opportunities for involvement with others in your community.

In Section 30, I recommend a small number of videos worth watching and books worth reading, and outline the contents of our website.

In Section 31, I invite your feedback: anything that will help us to update and improve further editions of this guide. You will also find mention of the presentations and workshops that I and others offer, along with information on ordering more copies of this guide.

Helpful endnotes are to be found in Section 32, and Section 33 contains the index.

This may sound like a lot, and it is. But it is also essential because so much may depend upon your grasping these points.

Our provincial and local governments are pressing ahead, in spite of public indifference, with refining their emergency procedures, seismically upgrading our infrastructure, and improving the ability of the emergency services to handle a colossal disaster. They know that a megaquake will occur. They probably want there to be as little egg on their faces — and our faces — as possible when it happens. Were the Big One to hit us tonight, no one could say that as a province we had done nothing — only that we had not done nearly enough in the decades we have had in which to become ready.

Southwestern British Columbia could be the most earthquake-prepared corner of the world, a shining example of how a society can get its act together. Instead — unless something changes drastically — we are an embarrassment waiting to happen, a disaster that will blight many of our lives, titillate the rest of the world for a few days, and elicit more sympathy than perhaps we deserve.

PUBLIC APATHY

QUESTION

Why do otherwise smart people living in southwestern British Columbia fail to prepare for something as inevitable as the Big One?

ANSWER

Ignorance, perhaps, of the fact that gigantic earthquakes really do happen here, even if we weren't around for the last one — but mostly denial.

Denial is the unconscious defence mechanism that protects us from painful thoughts and facts. It is the syndrome that allows people to drive without wearing a seatbelt, smoke tobacco, have unprotected sex, and in countless other ways fool themselves that "it won't, or couldn't, happen to me."

It is the root of many of humankind's entirely predictable misfortunes. It will account for massive numbers of lives that will be blighted, knocked sideways, and in many cases wiped out altogether here in BC — by what? By a "natural disaster" that need not have been anything like as disastrous as it probably will be.

If you live more or less outside of this denial box — or are willing to step outside it long enough to become earthquake prepared — congratulations!

Section 1
PREPARATION

A MAJOR EARTHQUAKE — IF YOU GET to experience one — will probably be the most dramatic and terrifying thing to ever happen to you. How you emerge from it will have a lot to do with three things:

- **where you are when it happens**

- **the swiftness and accuracy of your immediate responses** (and your actions in the subsequent hours, days, weeks, and months)

- **how well prepared you were ahead of time**

There is little that you can do about the first of these three, but the other two are entirely up to you.

Most people will react to the Big One just as they would to any other major disaster — in bewilderment and desperation. For the most part, they will act inappropriately. The foolish decisions that they make and the devastating experience that most of them will have will stem directly from their being unprepared. They never believed it would happen, or that if it did, it would be this horrifying.

Two kinds of foresight will make all the difference:

FORETHOUGHT

1. **mental forethought** — thinking the Big One through in advance, rehearsing it in your mind, practising the kinds of responses that will give you immediate advantages during an emergency.

2. **nuts and bolts forethought** — the actual stocking up and preparation that will provide you with the infrastructure and resources you will need to ride out the aftermath of a great quake.

These two kinds of forethought will greatly increase your chances of surviving the quake and coping gracefully with the days and weeks that follow.

When the Big One happens, it will be the real thing. There will be no second chance to get it right. If you haven't practised ahead of time, in your mind and on the ground, you will not instinctively know how to avoid being buried by a falling ceiling, to avoid those slicing shards of glass, to recognize the quake while driving and recognize the safest

REHEARSING

place to stop. You won't instinctively yell to others on the beach to head immediately inland to avoid the inevitable tsunami. And some hours later you will not recognize instinctively the signs of hypothermia in someone who is shivering uncontrollably in the rain and the cold.

Be familiar with the safe areas throughout your home, workplace, school, etc. — away from windows and glass (including mirrors) and anything heavy that may fly at you or crush you. Practise (and get everyone else in your household to practise) diving for cover. If taking cover is not instinctive, the chances are that it will not happen quickly enough or effectively enough when the time comes. The moment the Big One hits is not the time to wonder, even for an instant, what to do.

Until you have dived as fast as you can under your dining room table at home or under your desk at work, and held on; unless you have sat on the floor of a narrow corridor with your back against one wall and your feet braced against the other, with your arms over your head and face; unless you have imagined yourself crouching in front of your seat in the movie theatre, or hugging a utility pole, or covering your head with your arms as you try to evade falling items in the street; unless you have become used to selecting safe spots (or the safest spots available) in all kinds of situations, you will be at unnecessary risk when the big jolt happens.

Become familiar with this guide and there will be very little about a major earthquake and its aftermath that you will not be able to handle.

> Many years ago, as a 19-year old subaltern in the 2/6th Queen Elizabeth's Own Gurkha Rifles on counter-insurgency operations in the jungles of what is now Malaysia, I learnt from my brother officers to yell (from time to time, in appropriate settings), *"Goli ayo!"* Loosely translated, this meant, *"We're under fire!"* and every Gurkha soldier within earshot would hurl himself into a defensive position from which to return the imaginary fire. It was just an exercise, but it made for lightning-quick responses.

HARD TIMES Without the essentials and at least some of the comforts of everyday life, most people will be in for a rough time following the Big One. Civilized behaviour, the glue that holds society together in normal times, will begin to fragment. In many hearts there will be a deep anger and resentment, bred largely by fear, at what was not done beforehand, by us and by the authorities — that we allowed ourselves to get into this mess.

CHECKLISTS Most of the sections in this guide contain checklists. These are what make this book an action guide. They are indispensable. Use them to attain whatever level of preparedness you wish to achieve. They will show you what you have in place and what still needs to be done.

Check what you already own, or have lined up. Put an X against what you don't want, or what doesn't apply to you. As you will probably want to update these lists from time to time, consider using a pencil.

Custom-build your own system. If an Extreme Survivor suit sounds ridiculous to you, don't get one — but do decide what will keep you warm and dry in the conditions that you might face in the middle of winter. If you don't feel you need a bullhorn to communicate from your penthouse to rescuers below, or from your cabin to neighbours across the valley, don't buy one.

If nothing in a checklist applies to you — for example, you don't have a vehicle, workplace, or pets — then leave the boxes in that checklist empty, or put a line through the whole checklist. You won't need all of the items suggested and you won't need to follow all of the advice. But until you have honestly addressed every point in these checklists and done some quality thinking of your own, you won't be fully prepared.

Get started and you'll probably be impressed by how much you already have in place. As the saying goes, "By the yard it's hard; by the inch it's a cinch."

Store your emergency items in one or more specially designated spots in your home, at work, and in your vehicle — then leave those supplies intact. Immediately after the Big One, you won't want to discover that your roll of duct tape is almost finished, your heavy-duty work gloves are misplaced, your sleeping bags are at the cottage, and your cash reserve was spent on a recent outing.

INVENTORIES

In order to know exactly what emergency supplies you have and where they are located, you will need to maintain a simple inventory (or list of contents) for each location, container, or bag. Inventories are like finalized checklists. Ideally, they should be typed. They should be placed in plastic sheet protectors and stored with the supplies they describe. If you keep them up-to-date, you'll never have to wonder what's in a particular container, bag, or location.

72 HOURS IS NOT ENOUGH

Earthquake literature usually recommends that we be prepared to be on our own for at least 72 hours. I don't know what anyone imagines will suddenly happen as day three ends. It's unlikely that the power will be back on, the supermarket shelves magically re-stocked, the streets cleared, and transportation flowing. It is likely that emergency services — police, military, local governments, hospitals, doctors, care workers, and rescuers of every kind, as well as our entire infrastructure — will be stretched to impossible limits for months to come.

I strongly recommend that you prepare to be self-sufficient for at least two weeks, ideally for a month or more — unless you want your welfare to be dependent upon what you may be able to borrow from neighbours and what you may be able to find at a grim, overcrowded emergency shelter run by desperately overstretched volunteers.

WHAT ABOUT THE COST?

"Can I afford all this?" you may wonder. The answer is, unequivocally, "Yes!" If laying aside a month's worth of water and suitable foodstuffs is more than you can currently afford, put aside enough for a few days. If a butane lamp and heater for every room in your home and sufficient fuel to run them for a month is beyond your means, buy an inexpensive carton of candles and plenty of matches and have warm clothing readily available. Many precautions cost nothing.

If you can't afford to get fully prepared all at once, do it over a period of months — or years, if necessary. If you can't afford to buy new, then buy used. As a friend of mine, Holly Stewart, wrote recently, many of the items recommended in this guide are available secondhand:

> You can find clean and barely used warm clothing, boots, utensils, and tools at Value Village and in Salvation Army thrift stores. You can get great secondhand outdoor equipment (sleeping bags, camp stoves, packs, etc.) at Cheapskates and Sports Junkies in Vancouver. For thorough listings, check the *SuperPages* under Secondhand Dealers and Consignment Sales.

For bargains, monitor the classified ads in *Buy & Sell* and your local newspaper. Old wool sweaters or pants can be just as warm as new ones. A tarp may substitute as a tent. A tired-looking but serviceable tote bag will be just as effective as a new, bright red pack with "Emergency Supplies" stencilled on the side — and less likely to get stolen. Be on the lookout for lemons, however: a 50-cent sledgehammer will indeed have limited value if the head keeps flying off or the shaft breaks, and a tent that leaks and cannot be fixed may have no value to you at all.

Whatever you do, don't let cost — or anything else — be an excuse for inaction. If it ever crosses your mind that you can't afford to take the necessary steps, please consider whether you can afford not to. Just about every aspect of your life, and the lives of those around you, is at stake!

GO FOR IT!

Giant Cascadia earthquakes have happened many times in the past and they will happen again. They are part of the price of living in earthquake country. Being thoroughly prepared is likely to make a dramatic difference for those of us who are here at the time. The differences between being prepared and being unprepared may be having an uncomfortable time and having a devastating time; being warm and being cold; being well-fed and being hungry; being uninjured and being seriously injured; living and dying. The benefits of being prepared are incalculable. They are far, far greater than the cost and effort involved.

Earthquake preparedness is ultimately an individual responsibility.

Section 2
DURING THE BIG ONE

Y OUR CHANCES OF SURVIVING A MAJOR earthquake are excellent, especially if you know how to conduct yourself during and after the quake, and have taken basic precautions ahead of time. That means thinking things through and preparing. Rehearsing may seem silly in normal times, but it will help.

The Big One is likely to last several minutes, the longest minutes of your life. It will probably start with a loud bang and a massive jolt — think of a Mack truck slamming into the side of your house — followed almost immediately by "a deafening sound like a freight train rushing through your head," as survivors of other megaquakes have described it. The ground will be rolling in every direction at once. Buildings will be swaying violently. Whatever you're standing, sitting, or lying on will be heaving dramatically. You will be thrown to the ground. Unless you are clutching onto something, you will lose your equilibrium and find it impossible to retain your balance. You may even be unable to crawl to where you want to be. It will probably be the most frightening experience of your life.

If pets and birds behave uneasily immediately before you feel the earthquake, it will be because the earthquake is already occurring. You won't have long to wonder what's making Rover so restless. Dogs and cats will bolt in terror.

On September 1, 1923, my father rode out the Great Kanto earthquake that, at 8.3 on the Richter scale, destroyed two-thirds of Tokyo and four-fifths of Yokohama, Japan. He did so by clutching a metal railway station pillar that he happened to be standing beside. He was 18 years old at the time, teaching English in Tokyo as a means of financing his way to Cambridge University in England. He never spoke of the quake in any detail when I was young, and by the time I would have been interested enough to probe further, he had died. The quake and the 40-hour fire storm that ensued killed 142,000 people, many in the most horrific ways *(see the excerpt from Sixty Seconds that will Change the World: The Coming Tokyo Earthquake, in Section 30, Useful Reading).*

THE RISKS YOU FACE

Quakes rarely kill people directly. You are about as likely to be swallowed by an opening in the ground as you are to meet a brontosaurus. Most of the deaths that will occur during and following a megaquake in southwestern British Columbia will be due to:

- **the collapse of man-made structures**
Elevated highways, bridges, tunnels, and walls will collapse and an alarming number of homes and public buildings, including schools and hospitals, will be destroyed or otherwise rendered unusable, according to the Provincial Emergency Program (PEP) and Canada Mortgage & Housing Corporation (CMHC) video, *Is Your Home Earthquake Resistant?* *(see Section 30, Essential Viewing)*:

  > In a major Vancouver earthquake, up to 30 per cent of wood-frame houses, 50–100 per cent of brick buildings, 30 per cent of low- and medium-rise buildings, and 20 per cent of high-rise buildings will be destroyed.

- **falling and flying objects**
Outside, trees, utility poles, and street light standards will topple. Signs, air conditioners, bricks, shattered glass, and other debris will rain from the sky. Sheets of glass will burst from office towers and fly considerable distances, decimating anyone they hit. Indoors, people will be injured — some seriously, others fatally — by toppling furniture, filing cabinets, hot water tanks and appliances, falling ceilings and staircases, and collapsing walls.

- **fires**
Numerous fires will be caused by ruptured gas and power lines and the spillage of flammable liquids. They will be all the more difficult to control because of extinguishers lost in the rubble, water mains and fire equipment rendered useless by the quake, and the inability of rescuers and emergency services to get there in time *(see also Section 18, Fire)*.

- **liquefaction**
The shaking caused by an earthquake can transform soft ground, mud, and loosely packed or very wet sand into a fluid substance. These sediments may vibrate literally like gelatin. When ground liquifies, it is unable to support the weight of structures built on it. Buildings and bridges may lose their footings, and buildings may lean or sink. These conditions are mostly found in river deltas and in uncompacted landfills.

- **flooding**
Liquefaction will contribute to the bursting of river dikes and serious flooding will likely result.

- **landslides**
Any steep terrain is likely to collapse, sending rocks, mud, and debris thundering down on whatever lies below. Buildings may be partially destroyed, vehicles and people buried, driveways and roads blocked, and highways completely severed.

- **tsunamis**

  A major earthquake on the ocean floor will trigger a tsunami (pronounced soo-nah-mee: in Japanese, the character tsu means "harbour" and nami means "wave"), a succession of seismic ocean waves that can travel up to 965 kilometres (600 miles) an hour in deep water and hit shorelines thousands of kilometres away at up to 60 kilometres (37 miles) per hour.

In the 9.5 magnitude Chile earthquake of May 22, 1960, the western edge of the South American plate (on which the whole of South America rests) lurched as much as 18 metres over the subducting Nazca plate along a front more than 965 kilometres (600 miles) long and more than 160 kilometres (100 miles) wide. In addition to the more than 5,000 people killed on the coast of Chile, and the estimated one million that were left homeless, that lurch created a tsunami that took 15 hours to reach Hawaii, where it killed 61 people and seriously injured 282. Seven hours later it reached Japan, 12,875 kilometres (8,000 miles) from its source, where it killed a further 122 people and did considerable damage.[8] Our Cascadia subduction zone is similar to the subduction zone off the coast of Chile.

Tsunamis are notoriously deceptive and unpredictable. A tsunami can arrive within minutes of a severe earthquake, but the danger period can continue for many hours. It may be preceded by a rise or fall in sea level. A number of relatively minor surges, just a few feet high and spaced perhaps 10 to 30 minutes apart, may be followed by a thunderous wall of debris-choked water that sweeps away boats, ships, buildings, vegetation, and people. Waves that may be insignificant at one place on a shoreline may be devastating a short distance away. *(See Section 3, After The Big One.)*

There are two kinds of tsunami that could affect our coast:

- **locally generated tsunamis**

  If a large earthquake displaces the sea floor near our coastline, the first waves may reach our shores within minutes and there will be no time for authorities to issue a warning. People on or near shorelines, or in low coastal areas, need to be aware of the tsunami risk and be prepared to move to higher ground or inland immediately and stay there until certain that the tsunami danger has passed (this may mean waiting to hear from an official source, which could be many hours).

- **distant-source tsunamis**

  A tsunami generated by a very large earthquake in another area of the Pacific Ocean could reach our shores many hours after the earthquake occurred. If this happens, it is likely that people living in vulnerable areas will receive an official warning. If you are in an isolated area, however, or away from home, you may not hear official announcements. If you notice a sudden drop or rise in sea level, or hear a roar, you should regard these as signs of danger and move to safety at once.

- **aftershocks**
  Major quakes are usually followed by aftershocks — often a dozen or more. These may be massive. The first aftershock may occur within a minute or two of the main shock, or days, weeks, or months later. Aftershocks frequently result in more structural damage and loss of life, with all of the risks described previously being reactivated.

IMMEDIATE RESPONSES

During a major earthquake you will be lucky to reach any point more than a few feet from where you were when the shaking started. Depending on where you find yourself, the following should be among your immediate responses:

INDOORS

- **Dive for cover** at the very first rumbling, bang, or jolt. Don't hesitate. Dive for cover! If it turns out to be just a garbage truck hitting a giant pothole, you can laugh about it later.

- **Get under a solid table or desk, and hold on**. Be prepared to move with it.

- **In any exposed situation**, sit or kneel and bend forward with your forearms covering the back of your head and neck.

- **In an open archway or narrow corridor**, sit with your back against one wall and your feet braced against the other, bending forward with your forearms covering the back of your head and neck. A doorway is not a safe place to shelter because the door will swing violently.

- **Avoid being where unsecured, top-heavy objects** (dressers, filing cabinets, grandfather clocks, bookshelves, etc.) **may topple onto you**. *(See Section 12, Securing Your Home.)*

- **Avoid being where heavy items of any sort** (televisions, microwave ovens, the contents of kitchen cabinets, ornaments, etc.) **may fly across the room at you**. *(See Section 12, Securing Your Home.)*

- **Avoid unprotected windows and unsecured mirrors**. They'll likely end up as flying shards of glass. *(See Section 12, Securing Your Home.)*

- **Avoid unsecured appliances** (refrigerators, stoves, etc.) **and hot water tanks** that could cannon into you and crush you. *(See Section 12, Securing Your Home.)*

- **In public places, take cover where you are, preferably close to a wall.** Stay calm and keep clear of panicking people. *(See Section 12, Securing Your Home.)*

OUTDOORS

- **In a street with low-rise homes or single houses, or in a rural area, get clear** of anything that might collapse, topple, or fall, such as buildings, street lights, telephone poles, trees, and power lines.

- **Conversely, take shelter** beside or under anything that might protect you from such hazards.

- **In a downtown, high-rise area, crouch** against a wall, vehicle, mailbox, or street light with your arms protecting your head and neck. Avoid exposure to flying glass and debris in any way you can.

- **If driving, pull over and remain in your vehicle**. Try to avoid being caught under bridges, overpasses, utility poles, streetlights, trees, or anything else that may collapse.

- **At the beach or on any ocean shoreline, move inland or to higher ground immediately** in order to get clear of a possible tsunami.

- **In a wilderness area, be alert** for falling rocks, landslides, and avalanches.

Wherever you are, hold on tight and don't despair. It may feel as though the shaking and pandemonium will never stop, but it will. It's when it does that your troubles may really begin.

ACKNOWLEDGEMENTS: Some of the material in this section has been drawn from the Geological Survey Branch, B.C. Ministry of Energy and Mines' brochure, *Earthquakes in British Columbia*, some from the Humboldt Earthquake Center (Humboldt State University, Arcata, California) booklet *On Shaky Ground*, and, in each case, it is reproduced with the source's kind permission.

DURING THE BIG ONE REVIEW

EVERYONE IN YOUR HOUSEHOLD HAS:
- **read this section thoroughly** ☐
- **thought through and practiced the immediate responses listed above** ☐
  — enough for them to be second nature when the time comes

DISTURBING FACTS

Four years after the Kobe earthquake of January 17, 1995 — which, at 6.9 on the moment magnitude scale and 7.2 on the Richter scale, was minor compared with what we should expect — 45 per cent of homes were still uninhabitable.

It is anticipated that in our next Big One:

- up to 30 per cent of wood-frame houses

- up to 50-100 per cent of brick buildings

- up to 30 per cent of low- and medium-rise buildings

- up to 20 per cent of high-rise buildings

will be destroyed — unless a lot of seismic upgrading is undertaken in the meantime.

Section 3
AFTER THE BIG ONE

THE SHAKING AND THUNDEROUS NOISE, quite unlike anything you have experienced, have stopped. A new but equally dreadful cacophony begins: the howling of every dog for miles around; the din of auto, building, and fire alarms; people yelling and screaming. The closer you are to the epicentre, the more shaken and disoriented you will be. People around you will be dazed, trembling, in shock; they may vomit or faint. Some may be badly injured. Others may be dead. You will be surrounded by debris and utter chaos. It will be a nightmare.

Being aware of these things and being well prepared will dramatically alter your experience — for the better.

DESOLATION

Even if your home is left standing, the mess inside will be almost indescribable. Everything that can topple — bookcases, cabinets, appliances, furniture — will lie jumbled with everything that can fly: television sets, audio equipment, ornaments, pictures, books, plants, toys, files, and the contents of every cupboard and shelf. The most vengeful gang of home invaders couldn't hope to accomplish such a thorough trashing in so short a time.

No one can possibly predict all of the places or circumstances in which you might find yourself immediately following an earthquake, but you can imagine a lot of them. You may be in bed. You may be in the shower, or in the yard. You may be at a friend's place, or in a restaurant. You may be on the way home from work, or on your way to the mall, or out hiking. You may be hurt, or just badly shaken. Wherever you are and whatever your state, you are likely to be surrounded by turmoil and by distressed and panicked people.

ACTION STATIONS

The procedures below are just some of those that you should follow — as best you can, in whatever order makes sense to you. You may find yourself undertaking half a dozen of these steps simultaneously, or having to take one critical step, such as evacuating a burning building, disregarding all else.

Assess your situation. Ensure your own safety and well-being, and, as far as you can, ensure the safety and well-being of those around you.

Then start into the process of salvaging your world:

- **check for injuries**
Are you okay, unhurt? Is everyone else in your vicinity all right? What about pets?

- **don't move a seriously injured person**
Unless someone is in immediate danger of further injuries, leave them where they are. Help them in whatever way you can *(see Section 16, First Aid)* and get more qualified help to them as soon as possible.

- **dress for action**
If the quake strikes in any situation when you are not fully dressed — when you are in bed, for example, or in the shower — get into suitable clothing and shoes as rapidly as possible. This is when you should have a pair of strong shoes and heavy-duty workgloves at hand — and, at night, a flashlight. There will be broken glass and debris everywhere. You will need to be able to move around safely and confidently. One serious cut could render you useless.

- **check for signs of fire**
Use fire extinguishers and any other available means to put out small fires. If a fire is uncontrollable, evacuate the premises immediately, ensuring that others do the same. Seize your grab-and-go bag as you leave — if you can safely do so. *(See Section 15, Grab-and-go Bags.)*

- **avoid explosions**
If you are in a building supplied by natural gas, don't light a match, smoke a cigarette, use a regular flashlight, or operate any switch or electrical appliance until you are sure that there is no escaping gas. Any of these actions could cause an explosion. *(See Section 20, Natural Gas.)*

- **check for signs of escaping gas**
The signs are a hissing sound and a "rotten egg" smell. Only turn off the gas supply if you believe that gas is escaping *(for instructions on how to do this, see Section 20, Natural Gas)*. Important: once a gas supply has been turned off, it should only be turned back on again by a licenced technician — and that could be weeks away.

- **check for signs of structural damage**
Be aware that weakened walls, ceilings, and staircases may collapse without warning, bringing down debris and possibly burying you and others. Do not attempt to enter (or move around) your home or any other building if it appears unsafe to do so. If you become trapped, the neighbours will be unable to call 911 to have you rescued, and they may be unable to rescue you themselves. Be alert — don't be a liability.

- **check for signs of electrical short circuits**

  If there are broken wires, signs of arcing, or the smell of burning rubber in your home, switch off the electrical supply. Stand to the side of the main switch and look away from it, so that if there is an arc, your face won't be burned. Don't turn the supply on again until you can verify that it is safe to do so. Stay well clear of broken or dangling electrical wires.

- **stay at least 10 metres (30 feet) away from downed power lines**

  Cordon off such areas in any way you can — preferably with "Do Not Enter" tape *(see Section 11, Tools)*. If you find yourself in a situation where electrical wires have come down around you, stand still. If you have to move, take very small, shuffling steps so that your feet never leave the ground and keep moving until you are clear of the danger.

- **replace telephone handsets**

  Don't waste time trying to dial out. The system, already shut down by the quake, will be further overwhelmed by people trying desperately (and unsuccessfully) to get in touch with friends, relatives, and emergency services — and, shortly after the quake, by well-wishers outside the area trying frantically to call into the disaster zone. Whenever it does become possible to call your "out-of-area contact number" *(see Section 22, Communications)* to report on your situation and receive word of anyone who was separated from you at the time of the earthquake, it may be on a payphone. These are likely to be operating sooner than other lines. That is why you should have at least $20 in quarters in every grab-and-go bag. *(See Section 15, Grab-and-go Bags.)*

- **if you are on or close to the coast, anticipate tsunamis**

  Tsunamis are huge, unpredictable, seismic waves *(see Section 2, During the Big One)*. The message is simple: immediately following a major earthquake, get clear of vulnerable shorelines — and keep clear. If possible, move to ground 30 metres (100 feet) or more above sea level, or go up to 3 1/2 kilometres (2 miles) inland, depending on the topography and what obstacles there are (such as substantial buildings) to break the ongoing rush of a tsunami. If you have a vehicle and have the time to use it, by all means do so, but because of traffic chaos, damaged roads, downed power lines, and other debris, you may have to travel on foot. As a last resort, if evacuation is impossible, seek shelter on the third floor or higher of a reinforced concrete building if there is one close by, or in the upper branches of a substantial tree.

  Return only when official notification is received that the danger has truly passed. All too often, shortly after evacuees have assumed the danger is over and returned to the shoreline, a fatal wave has overtaken them. Since 1946, six tsunamis have killed more than 350 people on the West Coast of North America and the shores of Hawaii and caused 3/4 of a billion dollars in damage.

Be concerned about saving your life and the lives of others, not your possessions.

> Whatever you do, don't go looking for a tsunami. By the time that tsunami danger is obvious, it will be too late for you to escape it. Survivors of major quakes have a tendency to go sightseeing — including standing on shorelines hoping to see some action. The results can be fatal.

- **anticipate aftershocks**
  These are a series of perhaps a dozen or more, usually diminishing earthquakes that follow a major earthquake. They will be as unpredictable as the original quake and they're bound to cause further damage and distress. They may occur within minutes, days, or months of the original earthquake.

- **obtain help, offer help**
  If you need assistance, it is most likely to come from whoever happens to be around you. Emergency service workers will be fighting major, probably uncontrollable fires, and conducting search and rescue operations wherever they are most needed. Hospitals — those parts of them that are still operational — will be stretched far beyond their limits. Public service personnel will all have concerns of their own, and some will not be at their posts.

  If you are uninjured and still functioning, your help will be vital to others. Whether that means painstakingly removing rubble in order to reach an injured person, or boiling water for hot drinks and pondering how to feed those in your vicinity, or patching your or someone else's home in readiness for the long nights and days ahead, there will be plenty to do.

- **don't use or flush toilets**
  Unless you are sure that sewer lines are intact, flushing will only add to contamination of your surroundings. In an urban setting you will have no idea what is or isn't damaged, so hold off until the situation becomes clear. When you have a moment, set up a Camosun commode *(see Section 9, Sanitation)* or whatever other alternative sanitation you can create. When you have time, bail the water out of toilet tanks and retain it: you're going to need it *(see Section 4, Water)*.

- **turn off the water supply to your home**
  Do this in order to prevent possible contamination of the water supply already in your pipes or hot water tank *(for instructions, see Section 4, Water)*. If pipes are broken and there is flooding, be prepared to capture in containers as much run-off water as possible.

- **fill your bathtub with water**
  This will access precious water remaining in the plumbing.

- **do not use an elevator**
  You will be trapped inside if the power goes out.

- **consider staying put**
  If you feel secure where you are and you don't need to be somewhere else, weigh the odds carefully before moving. You may not be able to get to your intended destination anyway. Streets and roads are likely to be blocked; bridges and overpasses may have collapsed; debris and distraught people will be everywhere. There will be widespread fires: whole communities may be ablaze, and there will be forest fires. Ruptured water lines in some areas will make firefighting all but impossible.

- **leave a prominently-displayed note**
  If you do need to leave your home, workplace, or vehicle, others may be anxious to know how you are and where you've gone. Write your name clearly and in full (for people who do not know who "Mom", "Dad", or "Pete" is). State when you left, where you are headed, and when you may return (see Section 22, Communications).

- **clearing up**
  It is now that you will begin to appreciate the value of at least one pair of heavy workgloves for every active member of your household — and also value the strength of outdoor garbage bags. Strong garbage bags will be at a premium; you can't have too many of them in your emergency reserves.

CAUTION:
- Objects are likely to fall out of any closets and cupboards that may have remained closed during the earthquake.
- Try to package broken glass and china and other sharp objects in such a way that they will not be a further hazard — bound in many layers of newspaper, or in cardboard boxes.

- **secure your home, workplace, and vehicle**
  If you have to leave any of these (and you may need to do so in a hurry), there will be the possibility of unauthorized entries and looting. Secure them as best you can.

- **expect the best and worst of people**
  Acts of heroism, generosity, selflessness, and altruism will abound, as well as behaviours based on fear, anger, self-preservation, greed, and opportunism.

- **expect there to be feelings of anger, grief, loss, bewilderment**
  You've been through a disaster: so has everyone else. You are likely to be in a disaster situation for a long time, as are those around you. You have all been very badly shaken. You may tremble and feel numb. Some people will vomit or faint. Many will be in shock (*see Section 16, First Aid*), barely able to function. Some will panic. There will be erratic behaviours of every sort, along with grief, resentment, irritation, and apathy. Talk about what's happened. Allow others to share their feelings and experiences. What's happened has happened. Everyone's task now is to handle the situation as skillfully and resiliently as possible.

- **children will be particularly afraid and anxious**
  A child's biggest fear will most likely be that what just happened will happen again, and that they or you may get hurt, or be killed or separated from family or home. They may be right, because there will be aftershocks. Be calm, comforting, understanding, and reassuring. Share your plans and involve children in what must be done.

Wherever you are and whatever you are doing at the time, your life will be seriously turned upside down. That's why preparing yourself now is so important — to minimize the disaster in every way possible.

RETURNING TO NORMAL

Huge strides towards earthquake preparedness have been made by provincial and local governments, emergency services, utility companies, and other organizations, but their task is an impossible one. No matter how valiant and well co-ordinated the rescue, welfare, and reconstruction efforts, there will be incredible chaos and confusion. Thousands of people will have been killed. Many thousands more will have been injured. Countless numbers will be homeless, their lives and morale shattered. Thousands of businesses, ill-prepared for this disaster, won't survive. Depression and despair will set in for many people. It will take years for the region and its economy to recover.

My primary purpose in preparing this guide is to ensure that you and many others survive the quake and the days immediately following as comfortably as possible. For most, conditions following a major earthquake will be unbearable.

ACKNOWLEDGEMENTS: Some of the material in this section has been drawn from the Geological Survey Branch, BC Ministry of Energy and Mines' brochure, *Earthquakes in British Columbia*, some from the Humboldt Earthquake Centre (Humboldt State University, Arcata, California) booklet *On Shaky Ground*, and in each case is reproduced with the source's kind permission.

AFTER THE BIG ONE REVIEW

EVERYONE IN YOUR HOUSEHOLD HAS:
- read this section thoroughly _____ ☐
- been through the above procedures often enough ☐
  for their responses to be second nature when the time comes

The following are excerpts from the business column of *The Vancouver Sun* of February 18, 2000:

ARE YOU READY FOR THE BIG ONE?

A massive earthquake ravaged the West Coast 300 years ago. On the record, the next one could happen at any time and it wouldn't have to be a megaquake to do incredible damage. It's time to check your preparedness level....

About 60 per cent of homeowners in the Vancouver and Victoria regions carry earthquake shock coverage on their homes, says the Insurance Bureau of Canada....

Still, about 40 per cent of homeowners in BC's high-risk areas... face potential financial ruin if the earth moves.

Those whose homes are insured also face significant deductibles ranging from 5 per cent to 11 per cent of the replacement cost of the property....

[Canada Mortgage and Housing Corporation] estimates a major quake could destroy up to 30 per cent of wood-frame, single-family homes, 50 to 100 per cent of unreinforced masonry homes, up to 30 per cent of low- and medium-rise residential and commercial property, and up to 20 per cent of high-rise residential.[9]

Section 4
WATER

Adequate water is essential for all of your body's functions. Without water, a person will die within three to five days. Along the way they will experience increasing thirst, apathy, nausea, difficulty in breathing, dizziness, and delirium.

Most of us drink far too little water at the best of times. The last thing we need in the weeks following a major earthquake is to become dehydrated. This will be a time when health, strength, and mental clarity could be vital for survival.

The Big One will wipe out conventional water supplies across much of southwestern British Columbia and the Pacific Northwest of the United States. One of your top priorities (along with safety, food, shelter, and sanitation) will be access to drinkable water. It is a commodity that will be in great demand.

Normally, most "suspect" water can be treated *(see below)*. In the shake-up of a megaquake, however, man-made chemicals will find their way into groundwater and pipes on an unprecedented scale, resulting in water that could normally be purified becoming untreatable. There will also be microbial contamination, because sewage pipes will break and impact water sources.

IRREVERSIBLE CONTAMINATION

When water is obviously contaminated — when you can see the tell-tale swirls of gasoline on its surface, for example — you are unlikely to be in any doubt as to its toxicity. Following the Big One, the trouble will be in knowing whether water that looks all right is in fact treatable. It may or may not be; you will have no way of knowing.

Until safe supplies are shipped in, the only water that you will be able to count on will be:

- **factory-sealed, bottled drinking water** that has been properly stored and has not exceeded its maximum shelf life.

- **water that you have effectively bottled yourself** within the last three months and stored in suitable containers under suitable conditions.

- **water from other sources that you are confident could not have become contaminated** and that you are able to treat effectively.

FACTORY-BOTTLED WATER   You should have enough sealed, factory-bottled water — or, second best, water that you have effectively containerized yourself — to carry your household through at least the first two weeks following a major quake. Ideally, there will be enough to get you through the first month or more. Allow 5 litres (170 ounces) per person per day — 2 litres (70 ounces) for drinking and 3 litres (100 ounces) for cooking, washing, and cleaning. That's at least 70 litres (18.5 gallons) per person for a two-week supply.

> Your body loses about 2.5 litres (85 ounces) of water per day. That loss must be made up by fluids consumed and through your body's metabolic processes. You could survive for a while on much less than 2.5 litres a day, but you will want to do more than just survive.

The most convenient, readily available choices for your home, workplace, and vehicle reserves will probably be:

- **small pack bottles**
  These come in 500 ml, 1 litre, 1.5 litre, 2 litre, and 4 litre (17 ounce, 34 ounce, 51 ounce, 68 ounce, and 136 ounce) sizes and are highly portable. If obtained from a reputable bottling company and properly stored, they have a shelf life of at least two years.

- **water cooler bottles**
  These come in 11.3 litre (3 gallon) or 18.9 litre (5 gallon) sizes. They are less portable than the small pack bottles, but much more rugged. If obtained from a reputable bottling company and properly stored, they will have a shelf life of about six months.

Bottling companies have different grades of water (for example, spring, distilled, and reverse osmosis). Go for the best available.

SHELF LIFE   The reason factory-sealed small pack bottles have a shelf-life that is longer than factory-sealed water cooler bottles is that they are single use — they have not been used before. Water cooler bottles are sterilized and reused again and again by bottling companies. However carefully the recycling process is conducted, there is a risk of bacterial contamination that doesn't exist with pristine bottles.

The two-year and six-month shelf-lives quoted above can be considerably extended if you don't mind ending up with water that, while being safe to drink, is steadily losing its taste and aesthetic appeal. The time would come when you would want to treat such water (*see below*) — but you would be treating water that you know to be free of any chemical contamination.

(For three-gallon containers of water with a shelf life upwards of three years, see Resources on our website, www.earthquakeprep.ca.)

Store your drinking water reserves:

• **in cool, dark places that are likely to be accessible following the quake** (avoid exposure to direct daylight because UV light can deteriorate some plastic containers)

• **away from exhaust fumes and toxins such as gasoline and pesticides** (these vapours will penetrate plastic over time)

• **where they will not freeze** (unless you are specifically building ice-blocks — *see below*)

• **not directly on concrete** (which will leach chemicals into the water and eventually degrade the container)

Small pack bottles, because of their relative fragility, should be stored (where possible) in their original cases, in locations where they are unlikely to be crushed.

You should have sealed, factory-bottled water suitably stored:

• **at home**
Store as much as your space, budget, and sense of urgency will accommodate, and then some. This is going to be an invaluable commodity: you can't have too much of it. Most people are not going to be taking these precautions, so reliable water will be like liquid gold.

• **in your workplace**
Adequate reserves. How much will depend on the set-up there *(see Section 13, Workplaces)*.

• **in your vehicle**
Adequate reserves. You have no idea how long you and others may be trapped on the wrong side of downed bridges or blocked highways with nothing but the supplies in your vehicle *(see Section 14, Vehicles)*.

• **in your grab-and-go bag**
Adequate reserves. How much you pack away will depend on your sense of priorities and your carrying power *(see Section 15, Grab-and-go Bags)*.

You could, at this point, sit back knowing that your water needs are taken care of — but read on! We all need to know what our alternatives are and have back-up systems in place. What follows may look daunting, but it's easier than it looks.

ADDITIONAL SOURCES OF WATER

You should have clearly identified in your mind additional sources of water that will be safe for drinking and cooking — once you have effectively treated it *(see below)*. These sources might include:

- **faucets**

  As soon as possible after the shaking stops, use tap water to fill bathtubs, sinks and other suitable containers. Hurry, because your good fortune may not last long. Water may cease to flow from faucets or become contaminated — visibly or, much worse, invisibly.

- **standing water in pipes**

  Assuming that water pipes are not broken, there will be a useful supply of water in the pipes waiting to be tapped. Follow these three steps:

  1. Shut off the main water valve to prevent contamination; then open a faucet on the top floor.
  2. Open a faucet on the lowest available floor below to collect water. Have your container(s) ready.
  3. Close all faucets again to avoid flooding when water supply is restored.

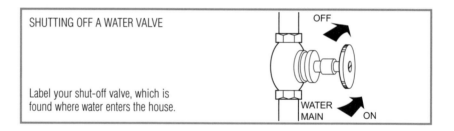

SHUTTING OFF A WATER VALVE

OFF

Label your shut-off valve, which is found where water enters the house.

WATER MAIN   ON

- **toilet tanks (but not toilet bowls)**

  Water in toilet tanks should be treatable as long as it has not been previously treated with one of those blue or green (or any other) disinfectants, or unless flushing of the tank has allowed possibly contaminated water to enter the tank. Scoop the water out and purify it before drinking. The quality of the water in your tanks will be improved if you regularly scrub the insides of the tanks with a brush used solely for that purpose.

- **hot water tanks**

  If your tank has remained upright, or even if it has toppled but retained some of its contents, it will be a valuable source of emergency water. If you have the foresight to flush your tank from time to time before an earthquake strikes, it will be less full of sediment when the time comes — and you will be familiar with the draining process. Follow these 6 steps:

  1. Turn off the electricity or gas to the tank.

2. Place a shallow container (such as a cake pan) under the drain cock at the bottom of the tank to catch water.
3. Open the drain cock (by hand) long enough to flush any sediment from inside the bottom of the tank — then close the drain cock. Retain the mucky water for washing purposes.
4. Turn off the cold water supply to the tank (to protect the contents of the tank from possible contamination).
5. Open a hot water faucet (preferably on the floor above the hot water tank).
6. Place a clean, shallow container under the drain cock and draw off water as needed.

(*For instructions on securing a hot water tank, see Section 12, Securing Your Home.*)

- **tarp water catchments**
  Have on hand at least one clean, undamaged, lightweight tarp with eyelet holes in each corner and along the sides. Use it to catch rainwater or to melt snow. Set up your water trap in a yard or on a patio, balcony or flat roof. You will need lengths of strong cord (and perhaps some strong cup hooks) from which to suspend the tarp.

- **suitable streams**
  A suitable stream might be one with nothing but wilderness upstream.

- **suitable ponds**
  A suitable pond might be one containing water that is not obviously fetid and that is unlikely to have been contaminated from surrounding sources.

- **protected springs and covered wells**
  Bear in mind that water from these sources may become contaminated hours or days after the earthquake because of the ground movement — for example, when nearby sewage pipes or manure pits fail.

- **water barrels**

> China has an extensive network of wells which are used to monitor water table fluctuations. Short term, rapid fluctuations are often an early signal of earthquake activity.

You can drink water from the following sources without treatment:

- **water from canned vegetables**

- **Tetra Pak or canned juices**

- **melted ice cubes**

ICE BLOCKS: If you have space in your freezer, consider freezing water in plastic containers (or double-bagged in plastic, perhaps using suitably sized cardboard boxes to support the bags while the water freezes and to protect the blocks of ice thereafter). Because water expands while freezing, leave enough air in the containers to allow for expansion. Following an earthquake, your ice blocks will help to conserve whatever perishables you may be able to salvage from your refrigerator. And, as the blocks melt, they will provide you with clean drinking water. Water stored in this way should be replaced every 12 months.

WARNING: Do not drink water from swimming pools, hot tubs, or water beds. The chemicals in these cannot be removed and will be harmful to your health. Use only for washing and general sanitation.

PATHOGENS

Pathogens are the disease-causing organisms that we seek to eliminate from "suspect" water when travelling in the wilderness. They are invisble to the naked eye and may be odourless and tasteless. They can cause mild nausea and fever, or develop into more serious illnesses, such as severe diarrhea, hepatitis, or typhoid fever.[10]

The pathogens of most concern are (from largest to smallest in size):

- **protozoa**, including *Cryptosporidium* and *Giardia*, the causes of giardiasis or "beaver fever." All protozoa are larger than one micron.

- **bacteria**, which cause sicknesses such as diarrhea and dysentery and are present in water world wide. Most bacteria are around 0.5 microns in size, although some, such as *Campylobacter*, can be 0.3 microns and smaller.

- **viruses**, which cause illnesses such as hepatitis and polio.

WATER TREATMENTS

The following treatments work well for killing pathogens — for purifying water. These are the treatments that you might choose in normal times. They are not able, however, to purify water that has become chemically contaminated, either visibly or invisibly — and there is the strong possibility that in the aftermath of a major earthquake, water from all but the safest sources will become chemically contaminated. This is why it is so important that you have substantial reserves of sealed, factory-bottled water, or water that you have carefully bottled yourself *(see below)* — with one or more of the following purification methods as back-up.

- **boiling**
  This is by far the most reliable method of making water of uncertain purity safe for drinking.[11] It destroys all organisms, including *Giardia* cysts.

Boil the water vigorously for one to three minutes. At altitudes higher than 1,800 metres (6,000 feet), boil for three minutes. If you are treating pond water or other truly "suspect" water and can find no alternative, boil it for at least 30 minutes. Then allow the water to cool to room temperature. The resulting flat taste can be improved by pouring the water back and forth between two clean containers (assuming you can find two uncontaminated containers in the aftermath of a major earthquake), or by adding a pinch of salt to each litre (34 ounces) of water.

Disadvantages: this method consumes precious time and cooking fuel and, therefore, may not be practical in the aftermath of a megaquake.

- **chemical disinfection**
  Please note: chemically treated water is intended for short-term use only.[12]

tincture of iodine 2%
This inactivates bacteria and viruses but not all protozoa, especially *Cryptosporidium*.[13]

Dosage: according to the table below. Mix well and allow the treated water to stand for at least 30 minutes before drinking, or several hours if the water is very cold or cloudy. To ensure that *Cryptosporidium* is killed, the water must stand for 15 hours before drinking. If you are on the move, the "standing" water can be carried with you in a canteen or other sealed container, so this method is portable. The treated water should have a slight iodine taste. If not, repeat the procedure.

Disadvantages: the effectiveness of iodization depends on the pH of the water. Pregnant women, infants, children, and people with thyroid disease should not drink iodized water, but for most people it is low risk in the short term (two or three weeks).

Amount of water	Amount of chlorine bleach to add to =		Amount of tincture of iodine 2% to add to =	
	Clear water	Cloudy water	Clear water	Cloudy water
1 litre (34 ounces)	1 drop	2 drops	5 drops	10 drops
4.5 litres (1 gallon)	4 drops	10 drops	20 drops	40 drops
22.5 litres (5 gallons)	20 drops	50 drops	100 drops	200 drops

NOTE: 1 US gallon is equivalent to 0.83 British gallons

household liquid chlorine bleach (containing 5.25% sodium hypochlorite)

This may not kill some intestinal viruses and the parasitic organisms that cause giardiasis, amebiasis, and cryptosporidiosis.[14] Its germicidal effectiveness varies with the pH, temperature, and organic content of the water to be purified. While just about every emergency preparedness guide and booklet recommends this method, the literature, according to the Canadian Pharmacists Association and the US Centers for Disease Control and Prevention, supports iodination over chlorination when boiling is not feasible. Do not use scented bleaches, coloursafe bleaches, or bleaches with added cleansers, and do not use granular forms of bleach, because they are poisonous.

Dosage: use according to the table above. Mix well and allow the treated water to stand for 30 minutes before use. As with the tincture of iodine treatment above, you can be on the move while the water is "standing." The treated water should have a slight chlorine taste. If not, repeat the dosage and let stand for an additional 15 minutes before using.

Disadvantages: questionable efficacy and, while better than nothing, not good for your body. Liquid chlorine bleach loses its strength after about one year. If you have to use old stock, increase the amount. Two-year-old bleach should not be used.

- **portable devices**
  A variety of portable methods are available at wilderness outfitters and camping stores.

  microstrainer filters
  These filters physically remove pathogens. One-micron filters remove only protozoa; 0.5-micron filters stop protozoa and larger bacteria; 0.1 to 0.3 micron filters block protozoa and smaller bacteria, including *Campylobacter*. Since viruses are too small to consistently filter out, users of microstrainer filters are advised to disinfect the water after filtration with iodine or chlorine.

  purifiers
  These consist of filters and an iodine-impregnated resin element. Their greatest effect is against bacteria. The iodine will kill some viruses, but the contact time with the iodine in the filter is too short to kill *Giardia* in cold water and will not kill *Cryptosporidium*. A purifier's final carbon stage removes most of the iodine before drinking.

  Advantage: under normal travelling and wilderness conditions, these devices provide almost instant drinkable water — just "pump and serve."

Disadvantages: relatively expensive, heavy, and bulky with moving parts, they require proper selection, operation, care, and maintenance if they are to produce safe water.

- **purification tablets**
  Pharmacies and outdoor or camping equipment suppliers sell small bottles of these iodine-based, germicidal drinking water tablets.

  Advantage: inexpensive, lightweight, and highly convenient.

  Disadvantage: not good for your body, these should only be used short term — in emergency conditions. They should not be used by children, pregnant women, or people with thyroid disease.

  Cloudy water should be allowed to stand long enough for the sediment to settle before treatment. Otherwise, use coffee filters, cheesecloth, or layers of any other clean, finely woven cloth to filter out as much sediment as possible before purifying the water.

> WARNING: Be extremely cautious about eating or drinking anything from an open container near shattered glass. Strain suspected liquids through coffee filters, cheese cloth, or any other clean, finely woven cloth.

WATER CONTAINERS

If you are going to bottle water yourself, make sure that the containers are:

- **as strong as possible** — glass and flimsy plastic containers are likely to break during a major earthquake, unless they are very well packed.

- **as opaque as possible** — the less transparent the container, the less its contents will be damaged by ultraviolet light.

There are excellent water storage containers available from wilderness outfitters and camping stores. But be warned: these containers, while they are ideal for brief camping trips and the like, are not designed for long contact with the bleach and iodine commonly used to sterilize water *(see above)* — which is another reason why stocking up with factory-bottled water makes such good sense.

> CAUTION: The plastic milk containers sometimes suggested in earthquake literature are not suitable for long-term storage of drinking water. They are designed to be kept in the fridge for a week and then recycled.

If you choose to go the home-bottled route — using ordinary tap water to fill thoroughly washed, well-sealed containers yourself — then change the water and sterilize the containers every three months (six months is too long). If you are not disciplined enough to change the water and re-sterilize containers that often, you will risk having fetid water reserves — not necessarily dangerous, but increasingly unpalatable.

Clearly label each home-filled container "water" and include the date when it was filled. Use a self-adhesive or tie-on label. Writing with a waterproof marker directly onto the plastic may contaminate the contents.

Store filled containers according to the instructions for factory-bottled water *(see above)*.

FRESHENING CONTAINERS

To freshen a drinking water container, use baking soda. Add one tablespoon of baking soda per 2 litres (68 ounces) of tap water. Close the cap and shake vigorously. Remove the cap, rinse the container thoroughly with more tap water, and then seal the container tightly.

STERILIZING CONTAINERS

To sterilize a drinking water container, use household liquid chlorine bleach (containing 5.25% sodium hypochlorite) or tincture of iodine 2%. Do not use scented bleaches, coloursafe bleaches or bleaches with added cleansers. Do not use granular forms of bleach, because they are poisonous. Add one teaspoon of bleach or tincture of iodine 2% per four litres (one gallon) of tap water. Close the cap, shake vigorously and let stand for three minutes. Remove the cap and pour out the sterilizing solution. Then rinse and rerinse the container several times with tap water before air drying the container and then sealing it tightly.

Following a major earthquake, things will be quite different. You will probably not have clean water to squander in this way. Containers will rapidly become recontaminated — even by the untreated water used to clean them.

TIP: Tape a dropper to each container of household bleach or tincture of iodine. That way you will have a dropper readily available when you need it.

WATER POUCHES

These almost indestructible packages contain 125 ml (4.2 oz) of purified water — a pretty meagre ration. But if you are looking for lightness (for example, in a grab-and-go bag) and convenience (they have a shelf life of at least five years), they could be excellent choices. They fit into pockets and other small spaces, and 24 of them add up to 3 litres of water. You can obtain these emergency reserves from survival equipment specialists *(look under Earthquake Preparedness, First Aid Equipment & Supplies, and Survival Equipment & Supplies in the SuperPages, or see Resources on our website, www.earthquakeprep.ca)*.

REFERENCES: The Canadian Pharmacists Association's *Compendium of Pharmaceuticals and Specialties*; the US Centers for Disease Control and Prevention's *Risks from Food and Drink*; Mountain Equipment Co-op's Spring & Summer 2000 Catalogue; and others.

WATER CHECKLIST

This checklist is for water reserves in and around your home. For water reserves in your workplace, vehicle, and grab-and-go bag, see those checklists. Remember: you are unlikely to need all of the options listed below. Just check and implement the ones that feel right for you.

FACTORY-BOTTLED WATER

_____ x **small pack bottles** (1 litre/34 oz) ☐

_____ x **small pack bottles** (1.5 litre/51 oz) ☐

_____ x **small pack bottles** (2 litre/68 oz) ☐

_____ x **small pack bottles** (4 litre/135 oz) ☐

_____ x **bottle cooler bottles** (11.3 litre/3 gal) ☐

_____ x **bottle cooler bottles** (18.9 litre/5 gal) ☐

_____ x **water pouches** (125 ml/4.2 oz) ☐

_____ x _____ ☐

_____ x _____ ☐

_____ x _____ ☐

HOME-CONTAINERIZED WATER

_____ x **water packs** (__ litres/ __oz/gal each) ☐

_____ x **water packs** (__ litres/ __oz/gal each) ☐

_____ x **water packs** (__ litres/ __oz/gal each) ☐

_____ x **water packs** (__ litres/ __oz/gal each) ☐

_____ x _____ ☐

_____ x _____ ☐

_____ x _____ ☐

MEANS OF COLLECTING WATER

_____ x **tarp** ☐

_____ **m/ft cord** ☐

_____ x **strong cup hooks** ☐
(from which to suspend the sides of your tarp)

_____ x **plastic bucket** ☐

_____ x _____ ☐

_____ x _____ ☐

MEANS OF TREATING WATER

_____ x **water filter** ☐

_____ x **water purifier** ☐

_____ x **household liquid chlorine bleach** ☐
(with dropper attached)

_____ x **tincture of iodine 2%** ☐
(with dropper attached)

_____ x **water sterilization tablets** ☐

_____ x **coffee filters or cheesecloth** ☐
(for straining out sediment)

☐

☐

KNOWN SOURCES OF ADDITIONAL WATER

_____ x **bathtubs** ☐

_____ x **standing water in pipes** ☐

_____ x **toilet tanks** ☐

_____ x **hot water tanks** ☐

_____ x **water barrels** ☐

_____ x **springs or protected wells** ☐

_____ x **suitable streams** ☐

_____ x **suitable ponds** ☐

Use, but do not drink water from:

_____ x **swimming pools** ☐

_____ x **hot tubs** ☐

_____ x **waterbeds** ☐

WATER REVIEW

Everyone in your household is familiar with the contents of this section ☐

Everyone in your household knows how to:

> **shut off a water supply** ☐

> **drain standing water from pipes** ☐

> **obtain usable water from a toilet tank** ☐

> **drain a hot water tank** ☐

W ITHOUT ADEQUATE FOOD, YOUR LIFE immediately following a major earthquake will be miserable. Your strength and morale will ebb fast. You will rapidly become dependent upon others — people whose resources are as depleted as yours.

Within minutes of the Big One's final jolt, supermarket and corner store shelves will be stripped bare. Actually, it will be the aisles that will be cleared, because whatever was on shelves will now be strewn several feet deep across the floor. Hardware stores, wilderness outfitters, camping stores, and suppliers of everything else that people feel they need will also be stripped.

STRIPPED SHELVES

How these transfers of goods will occur is anybody's guess. Most stores will be in total chaos, without power and with employees more anxious to reach home than man the doors or check-out counters. Wherever transactions can be done in a civilized fashion, that will probably happen. But things will get out of hand. Looting is not a subject that many people are eager to talk about, but it will occur. The first priority of police in the days immediately following a major earthquake will be search and rescue and the saving of lives. Protection of property will be much lower on their list.

The foodstuffs that the public will be scooping off the shelves are resources that the Emergency Social Services will be hoping to requisition and distribute a day or two later through emergency shelters. Because of their extensive planning, they will also have access to warehoused food all over the region. Meanwhile, the best time to do your shopping is now.

You will need emergency food reserves for your home and for your workplace, vehicle, and grab-and-go bag. The checklist below is for your home reserves. *Section 13, Workplaces, Section 14, Vehicles, and Section 15, Grab-and-go Bags* have their own checklists.

EMERGENCY RESERVES

For your emergency reserves you will want foods that:

- **keep without refrigeration**
- **require little or no preparation**
- **require little or no water**
- **meet individual needs** (e.g., special diets, infant formulas, etc.)
- **meet individual tastes**

You will need to rotate or replace your emergency food reserves every three to six months *(see Section 27, Check-ups)*. Where possible, select items that you and your household enjoy and are used to, foods that you will be happy to eat when the time comes to rotate them.

If using cans, jars, and packages, try to have them in sizes that can be consumed in one meal, without leftovers.

Bear in mind that foods with a high sugar content will give you a quick energy boost, but they will not sustain this energy over the long run.

Make a note in your diary to carry out your first restocking process *(see Section 27, Check-ups)*. The last thing you will want is to discover spoiled foods as you prepare your first meal in your lopsided home or stranded vehicle.

PACKAGING Wrap packaged foods in foil and heavy plastic to protect them from spoilage. Wrap jars and bottled items in a similar fashion and pack them to prevent breakage. Store everything below 18°C but above freezing.

YOUR CHOICES Your menu choices will almost certainly be from the five categories outlined below. Each category has advantages and disadvantages. My guess is that you will quickly spot the ones that will best meet your needs:

(A) READY-TO-EAT — CANS, JARS, AND PACKAGED FOODS

These are the familiar items that one finds in any grocery store. They include:

- **canned**, ready-to-eat meats, fish, stews, spaghetti, cheeses, vegetables, baked beans, soups, sauces, fruit, milk, etc.

- **jars of jam**, preserves, pasta sauces, etc.

- **staples** such as oatmeal, pasta, rice, noodles, sauce mixes, soups, puddings, powdered milk, flour, dried legumes (peas, beans), drinks, juices, sugar, syrup, honey, peanut butter, salt, pepper, spices, tea, instant coffee, and whitener

- **packaged** items such as crackers, cookies, cereals, jerky, nuts, raisins, dried fruit and trail mixes

Advantages

- some items require no preparation, heating, or cooking; others require minimal preparation and cooking

- familiar, widely available, and relatively inexpensive

- considerable variety (with plenty of room for creativity)

Disadvantages

- limited shelf life of about one year — not a problem if you are disciplined enough to rotate your emergency supplies into your daily fare at regular intervals *(see Section 27, Check-ups)*

- heating or cooking required for some items

EXAMPLES OF SIMPLE, HIGH-ENERGY RECIPES:
- Add canned meat, canned vegetables, and a sauce to boiled pasta. Warm and eat.
- Add pineapple chunks and a small amount of mayonnaise to a can of mixed beans. Mix and eat cold.

(B) FREEZE-DRIED FOODS

These are pre-cooked meals (entrées and desserts) that simply require the addition of boiling water or, in some cases, minimal baking or simmering. You will find them at wilderness outfitters, camping stores, and survival equipment specialists *(for recommended retailers, see our website, www.earthquakeprep.ca)*. They include:

- **meats**, stews, soups, vegetables, and fruits

- **typical entrees**: Chicken Primavera, Sierra Chicken, Teriyaki Turkey, Beef Stroganoff, Mountain Chili, Mushroom Pilaf with Vegetables, Shrimp Newburg, Lasagna, and Spaghetti Marinara with Mushrooms

- **typical desserts**: Chocolate Fudge Mousse, Apple Crumble, Wild Rice Pudding with Mixed Fruit, Apple Brown Betty with Streusel Topping, and various cobblers

Advantages

- minimal preparation and heating required — very convenient

- lightness, due to low moisture content (2% compared to 25% for typical supermarket dry foods)

- wide selection; pre-measured, pre-packaged portions

- widely available

- excellent shelf life (at least five years)

Disadvantages

- water required for rehydration

- simple means of heating required

- relatively expensive (about $8.00 Cdn per entrée)

(C) READY-TO-EAT — SELF-HEATING MEALS

These palatable meals (you might even say delicious under the circumstances) require no matches, no fire, no stove, no utensils, no refrigeration, and no water. You could prepare one in under 15 minutes almost anywhere — literally bobbing down a swollen river astride a log, if you could maintain your balance.

As this guide goes to press, Hot Pack self-heating meals are the most readily available brand in Canada. They come in boxes measuring 21cm x 15cm x 4cm (8 1/4" x 6" x 1 1/2") and weighing about 265 g (8.5 oz). They are ideal for workplaces, vehicles, and grab-and-go bags *(see Section 13, Workplaces; Section 14, Vehicles; and Section 15, Grab-and-go Bags)*. The self-heating instructions are clear, but you should rehearse them carefully in your mind before proceeding. *(For Hot Pack retailers and other manufacturers, see Resources on our website, www.earthquakeprep.ca.)*

- **Hot Pack choices**: Beef and Chicken Stew, Chicken and Vegetable Casserole, Spanish Breakfast, Shepherd's Delight, and Rotini Bolognese

Advantages

- no cooking facilities needed — very convenient

- disposable plate, fork, napkin, salt, and pepper included

- available from survival equipment specialists

- excellent shelf life (at least five years, if not allowed to get too hot or cold in storage)

Disadvantages

- limited variety

- relatively expensive (about $8.00 Cdn per meal)

(D) DEHYDRATED FOODS

These come in oxygen-free cans and will typically be raw ingredients such as:

- **cereals** (wheat, barley, oats, etc.)

- **vegetables** (sweetcorn, broccoli, carrots, peas, beans of many sorts, celery, potato granules, mixed peppers, chopped onions, etc.)

- **fruits** (banana slices, apple slices, etc.)

- **other ingredients** (egg powder, milk powder, butter powder, margarine powder, cheese powder, tomato powder, etc.)

Preparing and cooking these foods takes more time, effort, and resources than most people will want to invest during the chaotic weeks following a giant earthquake — but this will be the route of choice (or necessity) for some people.

Emergency equipment suppliers will have some items on their shelves and will be able to order in more *(for recommended retailers, see Resources on our website, www.earthquakeprep.ca)*. Or, you might choose to process cereals, vegetables, and fruits yourself, sealing each batch of 100 per cent moisture-free, dehydrated food first in a light-proof mylar bag with a couple of oxygen-absorption packets, and then in a suitable, unused, food-grade, plastic container.

Advantages

- flexibility in terms of recipes
- economical
- long shelf life (10-20 years)

Disadvantages

- water required for rehydration
- substantial preparation required
- cooking facilities and adequate fuel essential

(E) READY-TO-EAT — "RAFT RATIONS"

These are Canadian Coast Guard and/or US Coast Guard approved survival rations. They are emergency meal replacements, designed to keep survivors in liferafts alive until help arrives. They are not everyone's idea of a square meal — that is not their purpose. Each one-day, two-day, or three-day pack contains life-sustaining compressed food bars closely resembling shortbread. That's it. You are likely to want these spartan meals if compactness and lightness are paramount — for example, in grab-and-go bags *(see Section 15, Grab-and-go Bags)*, or if you envision yourself being holed up somewhere — perhaps miles from anywhere in a stranded vehicle — with little to do but wait for help. You will want something more nourishing and substantial if you are going to be at all active.

There are three readily available brands, Datrex, SOS, and FAST, and you will be fine with any of them. The FAST three-day, vacuum-sealed pack, for example, consists of 18 x 43 g (1.5 oz), 200-calorie bars (3,600 calories in all). It measures 13.5 cm x 8.5 cm x 6.5 cm (5 1/4" x 3 1/4" x 2 1/2") and weighs 774 g (27 oz) — about three quarters of the size and weight of a brick.

Along the same lines, there is a Millennium Bar designed to be a single meal replacement. These 409-calorie bars come in six flavours and weigh 84 g (2.95 oz) each. *(These "raft rations" are available from survival equipment specialists.)*

Advantages

- compact, life-supporting, emergency nutrition

- long shelf life (at least 5 years)

Disadvantages

- minimilistic, survival rations, insufficient for sustained activity

At home you will have whatever you need in the way of cutlery, plates, bowls, cups, and utensils — and these items are covered in the *Section 13, Workplaces; Section 14, Vehicles; and Section 15, Grab-and-go Bags* checklists.

There is no way that you are going to have too much in the way of emergency food and other supplies when the Big One happens. If it isn't friends or relatives who will be knocking on your door (perhaps because they have been forced to abandon their homes), it will be ill-prepared neighbours. One way or another, your supplies will be in demand.

> WARNING: Be extremely cautious about eating or drinking anything from an open container near shattered glass. Strain suspected liquids through coffee filters, cheesecloth, or any other clean, finely-woven cloth.

FOOD CHECKLIST

This checklist is for food reserves in your home. Build up stocks that feel right for you. Then do the same for your workplace, vehicle, and grab-and-go bags.

_____ x _____ ☐
_____ x _____ ☐
_____ x _____ ☐
_____ x _____ ☐
_____ x _____ ☐
_____ x _____ ☐
_____ x _____ ☐
_____ x _____ ☐
_____ x _____ ☐
_____ x _____ ☐
_____ x _____ ☐
_____ x _____ ☐
_____ x _____ ☐
_____ x _____ ☐
_____ x _____ ☐
_____ x _____ ☐
_____ x _____ ☐
_____ x _____ ☐
_____ x _____ ☐
_____ x _____ ☐
_____ x _____ ☐
_____ x _____ ☐
_____ x _____ ☐
_____ x _____ ☐
_____ x _____ ☐
_____ x _____ ☐
_____ x _____ ☐
_____ x _____ ☐
_____ x _____ ☐
_____ x _____ ☐

The following excerpts are from an article in *The Vancouver Sun* of March 5, 2001:

YOU CALL THAT AN EARTHQUAKE? LAST WEEK'S TREMOR FROM SEATTLE DOESN'T EVEN REGISTER WHEN YOU COMPARE IT TO THE CATASTROPHES OF THE PAST FEW CENTURIES

If you thought that $2-billion earthquake Wednesday morning offered a taste of what the Big One has to offer, you'd be wrong. For all the damage to structures in Washington and the alarm felt by those in British Columbia and Oregon, at 6.8 on the Richter scale, the earthquake was a mere tremble compared to what is possible....

Think of it this way: what shook Seattle and Vancouver was about half the magnitude of the 7.3 earthquake centred on Vancouver Island's Mt Washington 55 years ago. That one released more energy than the atomic bomb that vapourized the Bikini atoll, reconfigured whole Gulf Islands, altered the contours of Comox Lake and caused large areas of sea bottom to subside by the height of a three-storey building, and the initial shock was powerful enough to toss a 25-tonne donkey engine into the lake....

An earthquake on one of the faults in the Strait of Georgia that was similar to the 1946 event, which released about 16 times as much energy as the one which just occurred in Washington, would clearly do more damage and the casualties might be in the tens of thousands. And an earthquake of that magnitude is just the start of the dire possibilities. In geological terms, events releasing 30 or 50 or 100 times more energy are not as uncommon on the West Coast as we like to think.

On average there's an earthquake at least as powerful as the recent Washington tremor every 10 years or so in the coastal zone from Puget Sound to the south coast of Alaska — and some of them make this one look like a popgun.

The greatest earthquake ever recorded in Canada — 8.1 on the Richter scale — occurred in Haida Gwaii in 1949. It released more than 40 times the energy of the Washington event and was of the same order of magnitude as the earthquake of 7.9 that killed 200,000 people in Tokyo and Yokohama in 1923 and the magnitude 8.1 event that devastated Mexico City in 1985. And both those quakes were at least 10 times smaller than the 9.5 and 9.2 monsters which rocked Chile in 1960 and southern Alaska in 1964. By way of comparison, those two earthquakes were at least 500 times bigger than last week's shake and released perhaps more than 10,000 times as much energy.

So, for all our media chatter about wake-up calls, most of us can't even begin to imagine what we might be in for if a great earthquake were to occur much closer to our high density population centres than we've so far experienced....[15]

Continued on page 72

Y OU WILL PROBABLY WANT TO KEEP YOUR emergency cooking to a minimum, and you will certainly want it to be as safe and efficient as possible. Or — using some of the options outlined in *Section 5, Food* (self-heating meals, emergency rations, canned foods, etc.) — you could manage with no cooking facilities at all.

Here are your available choices:

- **butane stoves**
  These are the ones that the chefs in most Sunday brunch buffet lines use. Safe enough to be used indoors (provided there is reasonable ventilation). User-friendly: just add a pressurized metal canister, light, and cook. Very portable around the home, but not portable enough for a grab-and-go bag (which won't matter if you stock your bags with self-heating meals). An excellent choice for many households, but not widely available. *(For retailers, see Resources on our website, www.earthquakeprep.ca.)*

- **propane (and butane/propane mixture) stoves**
  Widely available. Because of their carbon monoxide emissions, they should only be used outdoors or in well-ventilated areas (for example, in your yard, on your balcony, or indoors with the windows wide open, but not indoors in the middle of winter). *(Available at wilderness outfitters and camping equipment stores.)*

- **liquid fuel camp stoves**
  Some of these burn white gas only. Others burn a range of liquids including white gas, kerosene, diesel oil, aviation (piston engine) gas, and jet fuel. They require pumping, priming (pre-heating), and regular maintenance. They are ideal for camping and expeditions. If you already have one and are familiar with its demands and limitations, this may be the route for you. If you are not used to working with them and having them roar at you, overheat, and flare up, then settle for a tamer, more user-friendly option. *(Available at wilderness outfitters and camping equipment stores.)*

- **solid fuel camp stoves**
  Fine for heating liquids, simmering, and very limited cooking. Compact and portable. No liquid, no priming, no wicks, no pressure, no moving parts. Odourless, non-toxic fumes. *(Available at wilderness outfitters and camping equipment stores.)*

For further information, see *The Mountain Equipment Co-op Guide to Stoves* leaflet, obtainable from MEC stores or by calling 604 876-6221 or 1-800 663-2667.

- **barbecues**
  Fine outdoors, but never to be used indoors; they produce deadly carbon monoxide gases.

Do not count on your wood-burning fireplace or stove being usable in the aftermath of a major quake. It is likely that the chimney or flue will be damaged, in which case continued use of the fireplace or stove will allow deadly carbon monoxide to permeate your home. You will also run the risk of undetected fire getting into walls or other cavities — and erupting hours later.

You may be able to inspect most or all of your stove's flue, but you will be unable to inspect satisfactorily your fireplace chimney. If you feel that the shaking has been insufficient to damage the chimney or flue, and you have no other means of cooking or heating your home, you should take the following precautions — being aware that you may be taking a considerable risk:

1. Inspect the outside and inside of the chimney or flue as carefully as possible, using a flashlight.
2. Light a trial fire with newspaper and a small amount of kindling only. Immediately check all rooms, including any attic or roof space, for signs or smell of smoke.
3. If you decide to add further to the fire, do so in small amounts, continuing to monitor all rooms, including any attic or roof space, at frequent intervals. Please note: carbon monoxide is invisible and odourless, so you may have no means of detecting it without the help of a carbon monoxide (CO) detector *(see Section 19, Carbon Monoxide Poisoning).*
4. Keep one or more fire extinguishers and water on hand for putting out a fire, if necessary. The water is essential because on contact with the fire, it will produce steam. The rising steam will extinguish a fire inside the chimney or beyond the reach of a fire extinguisher.

Following any other kind of disaster, of course, your wood-burning stove or fireplace may be perfectly usable for emergency cooking and heating.

COOKING CHECKLIST

This checklist is for cooking facilities in your home. Cooking facilities for your workplace, vehicle, and grab-and-go bag are looked at in those checklists. Remember: you won't need all of the items in this checklist. Just check and implement the ones that meet your needs.

MEANS OF COOKING

_____ x **butane stove** ☐
    (to be used with adequate ventilation)

_____ x **butane/propane mixture stove** ☐
    (to be used outdoors or in well-ventilated areas)

_____ x **propane stove** ☐
    (to be used outdoors or in well-ventilated areas)

_____ x **liquid fuel camp stove** ☐
    (to be used outdoors or in well-ventilated areas)

_____ x **solid fuel camp stove** ☐
    (to be used with adequate ventilation)

_____ x **barbecue** ☐
    (to be used outdoors only — never indoors)

_____ x **wood-burning stove** ☐
    (do not count on this — *see above*)

_____ x **wood-burning fireplace** ☐
    (do not count on this — *see above*)

FUEL AND SUNDRIES

_____ x **butane canisters (227g/8 oz)** ☐
    (*see also Section 7, Lighting and Section 8, Heat and Warmth*)

_____ x **butane/propane mixture canisters** ☐
    (*see also Section 7, Lighting and Section 8, Heat and Warmth*)

_____ x **propane canisters (____g/____oz)** ☐
    (*see also Section 7, Lighting and Section 8, Heat and Warmth*)

_____ x **camp stove liquid fuel** ☐
    (___ hour supply) (describe fuel: _____)

_____ x **camp stove solid fuel** ☐
    (___ hour supply) (describe fuel: _____)

_____ x **barbecue fuel** ☐
    (___ hour supply) (describe fuel: _____)

_____ x **kindling and seasoned wood**
(in case stove or fireplace remain intact: _____ hour supply)

_____ x **regular matches**
(stored in a waterproof container)

_____ x **waterproof matches**

_____ x **wind and waterproof matches**

_____ x

_____ x

UTENSILS

kitchen utensils
(the ones you already have)

_____ x **sets of plastic plates, bowls, mugs**
(dishes may be broken in the earthquake)

_____ x **food wrap**
(to cover plastic plates, bowls — no washing)

_____ x **disposable paper plates, bowls**

_____ x **sets of disposable plastic cutlery**

_____ x **manual can opener with bottle opener**

_____ x **tin foil**

_____ x **paper towels**

_____ x

_____ x

_____ x

_____ x

_____ x

_____ x

_____ x

_____ x

_____ x

_____ x

_____ x

_____ x

YOU WILL ALMOST CERTAINLY BE WITHOUT power following a major earthquake. Safe, efficient emergency lighting will go a long way to brightening your life until power is restored. You will have difficulty functioning effectively without suitable lighting.

Bring together whatever combinations of emergency lighting appeal to you and meet your needs, bearing in mind the cautions expressed below. Distribute your choices between your home *(see the checklist below)* and your workplace, vehicle, and grab-and-go bag *(see Section 13, Workplaces; Section 14, Vehicles; and Section 15, Grab-and-go Bags)*. Have lots of spare batteries, canisters, and fuel on hand, as applicable.

Here are your options:

- **regular flashlights**
  Everyone in your household should have a flashlight in a drawer of their night table or on a secure hook — or wherever else they can count on finding it when the shaking stops. Important: if your home uses natural gas, at least one of your flashlights should be an "intrinsically safe" one, unless you choose to have one or more lightsticks on hand *(see Section 20, Natural Gas)*.

- **"intrinsically safe" flashlights**
  Operation of a regular flashlight creates a spark that could cause an explosion where flammable gases or vapours are present (for example, around a gas leak or a spill of flammable liquids). If you have a natural gas supply to your home or workplace, you may want to have at least one non-sparking, "intrinsically safe" flashlight on hand. They come in many sizes and styles, with a variety of UL (Underwriters Laboratories) and CSA (Canadian Standards Association) safety codings. They are usually orange in colour and are not widely available. Pelikan, Bright Star, and Energizer are brands to look for *(for retailers, see Resources on our website, www.earthquakeprep.ca)*. A lightstick is an alternative to one of these flashlights.

- **hand-powered flashlights**
  These flashlights need no batteries to function; you simply keep squeezing the handle for an always-available light source. A

DIRECTIONAL LIGHTING

disadvantage is that the moment you stop squeezing, the light goes out. Not widely available. *(For retailers, see Resources on our website, www.earthquakeprep.ca.)*

- **electric headlamps**
These headlamps are worn on the front of a lightweight head sling for hands-free operation. There is a wide range of models ranging in cost from about $10 to $80 Cdn, with different features, battery and bulb options, and burning times. *(Available from wilderness outfitters and camping equipment stores.)*

ALL-AROUND LIGHTING

- **electric lanterns**
These use four, six, or eight D-cell alkaline batteries. They are safe and convenient, with a wide range of models available costing from about $16 to $50 Cdn. Running times are up to 8 hours on high, 20 hours on low, and 100 hours as a nightlight. *(Available from wilderness outfitters and camping equipment stores.)*

- **butane lanterns**
Butane-burning appliances should be used indoors only with adequate ventilation. They are reliable, portable, and user-friendly, but not widely available. *(For retailers, see Resources on our website, www.earthquakeprep.ca.)*

- **propane (or butane/propane mixture) lanterns**
Because of their carbon monoxide emissions, these user-friendly lanterns are designed for use outdoors or in well-ventilated areas. Do not use indoors unless doors or windows are open. *(Available from wilderness outfitters and camping equipment stores.)*

- **wick lanterns**
These lanterns have been around since the days of the early settlers. The secret is to have a lamp with a decent burner and to use high-quality lamp oil that will not smell or smoke. Regular kerosene and paraffin will smell and smoke, as will any oil if you turn the wick up too high. Relatively safe: if you throw the lamp onto the barn floor, it will probably go out — unlike in the old Hollywood movies. Use with adequate ventilation (i.e., don't burn one in your airtight Volkswagen with the windows wound up). *(For retailers of the Dietz No.76 Lantern, an old-time, rugged performer, see Resources on our website, www.earthquakeprep.ca.)*

- **candle lanterns**
Simple and relatively safe. *(For retailers of Candlelier lanterns, which have three spring-loaded candles each with a burning time of six hours, see Resources on our website, www.earthquakeprep.ca.)*

- **candle(s)-in-a-can**
Virtually indestructible. Coghlan's 36-hour emergency candles come with three wicks, each producing up to 12 hours of light and some heat. *(Available from wilderness outfitters and camping equipment stores.)*

- **candle-in-a-jar**
Not recommended, because the chances of the glass jar breaking in a major earthquake are very high.

- **regular candles**
Inexpensive and versatile. Ideally, use short, squat ones. Candles are easily knocked over and they do cause fires. Consider stabilizing yours by duct-taping them to whatever you are standing them on or in. Consider long-burning, drip-free ones. Please note: candles may get broken in a major quake.

- **tea lights**
Inexpensive and versatile, they are virtually indestructible.

- **glow or lightsticks**
These are compact, lightweight, non-flammable, weatherproof, and non-toxic. They are not a source of ignition, so they can be used safely even in the presence of flammable substances or escaping gas. A good choice to have beside your bed if your home has a natural gas supply. They come in a variety of colours and produce all-around light for up to 12 hours once snapped. There is a yellow, high-intensity one that lasts for up to 30 minutes once snapped. Shelf life: four years (after which they may still be usable but with reduced output). They also make a good signalling device. *(Available from wilderness outfitters, camping equipment stores, home hardware stores, etc.)*

- **power failure lights**
When plugged into an AC outlet with the switch on auto, these inexpensive units will automatically turn on in the event of a power outage. The light that they give is minimal, but it may be exactly what you need at strategic points in your home or workplace in the critical minutes following an earthquake — or in the blackout that may follow any power failure. To use one of these units as a flashlight, simply unplug it from the wall and install a couple of AA alkaline batteries.

GASOLINE-POWERED GENERATORS: Unless you already have one, or need one to keep an appliance or equipment running regardless of expense and noise, a generator is likely to be more trouble than it is worth. Portables start at about $600 Cdn *(for recommended models, see Resources on our website, www.earthquakeprep.ca)*. Your supplier will help you to determine the size (number of watts) you need. You will need to have adequate reserves of gasoline safely stored *(see Section 28, Warnings)* and you might also invest in a small, multi-purpose pump that will enable you to draw further gasoline from any vehicle's tank.

LIGHTING CHECKLIST

This checklist relates to emergency lighting in and around your home. Your lighting needs for your workplace, vehicle, and grab-and-go bag are looked at in those checklists. Remember: you won't need all of the options in this checklist. Just check and implement the ones that meet your needs.

DIRECTIONAL LIGHTING

_____ x **regular flashlight** ☐

_____ x **intrinsically safe flashlight** ☐

_____ x **hand-powered flashlight** ☐

_____ x **electric headlamp** ☐

_____ x ☐

_____ x ☐

_____ x ☐

_____ x ☐

_____ x ☐

ALL-AROUND LIGHTING

_____ x **electric lantern** ☐

_____ x **butane lantern** ☐

_____ x **propane (or butane/propane mixture) lantern** ☐

_____ x **wick lantern** ☐

_____ x **candle lantern** ☐

_____ x **candle(s)-in-a-can** ☐
(see also Section 8, Heat and Warmth)

_____ x **regular candles** ☐

_____ x **tea lights** ☐

_____ x **glow or lightstick** ☐

_____ x **power failure light** ☐

_____ x ☐

_____ x ☐

_____ x ☐

_____ x ☐

_____ x ☐

_____ x ☐

SUNDRIES

_____ x **spare batteries (size _____)**

_____ x **spare batteries (size _____)**

_____ x **spare batteries (size _____)**

_____ x **spare batteries (size _____)**
(batteries should be stored separately from their units in a plastic bag)

_____ x **spare bulb (size _____)**

_____ x **spare bulb (size _____)**

_____ x **butane canisters (227 g/8 oz)**
(see also Section 6, Cooking and Section 8, Heat and Warmth)

_____ x **propane (or butane/propane mixture) canisters (_____g/_____oz)**
(see also Section 6, Cooking and Section 8, Heat and Warmth)

_____ x **container of lamp oil (size _____)**

_____ x **spare candles**

_____ x **roll (or folded sheets) of aluminum foil**
(to place under dripping candles or tea lights)

_____ x **regular matches**
(stored in waterproof container)

_____ x **waterproof matches**

_____ x **wind and waterproof matches**

_____ x **gasoline-powered generator**

_____ **litres/gallons of gasoline**
(safely stored — _see Section 28, Warnings_)

_____ x **multi-purpose pump**

_____ x _____

_____ x _____

_____ x _____

_____ x _____

_____ x _____

_____ x _____

LIGHTING REVIEW

**Everyone in your household is familiar with how to shut off an
electrical supply**

**The directory on the household fusebox (breakerbox)
is clearly readable**

The following excerpts are from an article in *The Vancouver Sun* of March 5, 2001:

continued from page 58

We know that a great earthquake was responsible for the single greatest natural disaster to face humankind. On January 23, 1556, what is now thought to be about a magnitude 8 event killed an estimated 830,000 people in the Shensi province of China. It is said that the prosperous region in mid-China suddenly fell silent and ceased remitting taxes. The emperor, fearing insurrection or invasion, sent an army to investigate. The general found only rubble and corpses over a vast area.

But better eyewitness accounts of what can happen when the shaking starts lie closer to home. On June 7, 1692, three earthquakes so powerful that they moved several mountains more than a kilometre from their original location, struck the island of Jamaica. The British colonial outpost of Port Royal suddenly sank 15 metres below the surface of the sea and the subsequent tsunami carried a British naval frigate across what was left of the townsite and deposited the ship inland.

One of the worst urban earthquake disasters, however, occurred at Lisbon, Portugal, on November 1, 1755. It [is] now thought to have been 8.5 or greater in magnitude and centred about 200 kilometres offshore.... In all, those crushed in the rubble, drowned by three successive tsunamis or burned in the subsequent fires are thought to have numbered 60,000.

Yet those casualty figures pale by comparison to the Tokyo earthquake [of] September 1, 1923 [when] a magnitude 7.9 earthquake struck... As shockwaves rippled through ground that rose and fell by as much as two metres, buildings began to collapse and a train carrying 500 commuters was hurled into the sea. Thousands of people who rushed into the streets were buried in falling debris.... A tank farm on shore disintegrated and flaming oil poured in behind the breakwater.... Against this hellish backdrop, 40,000 survivors rushed into an open area only to be asphyxiated by the fumes from the fires — which was a blessing for there was no way of escape and they were all burned in the firestorm.

The bottom of Sagami Bay suddenly sank by 100 metres and successive tsunamis pounded the shore, drowning thousands more and sweeping survivors out to sea. At the end of the first day, close to 100,000 were dead, more than 40,000 were missing, more than 100,000 were seriously injured, 2.2 million homes had been destroyed and 1.5 million survivors were without any shelter.

The Japanese government thought it was a natural catastrophe that would never be repeated — but it was, almost 50 years later on the other side of the Yellow Sea. On July 28, 1976, a magnitude 7.8 quake occurred... beneath the city of Tangshan in northeast China.... In a matter of seconds an industrial city of a million people was reduced to rubble. About 240,000 people perished and 7,000 families were completely obliterated.... When night fell again, the city of Tangshan had virtually vanished....[16]

Continued on page 88

THIS SECTION DEALS WITH MEANS OF keeping you and your home warm in the aftermath of a major earthquake. It also covers the importance of having warm clothing with you whenever you leave home. Assess what you already have in place, and then assemble whatever further items you feel will best meet your needs.

Keeping warm in your workplace and keeping warm in your vehicle are covered in *Section 13, Workplaces and Section 14, Vehicles.*

You will not need to heat all of your home, unless your home is very small. Use tarps or plastic sheeting (you will find these recommended at various points in this guide) to seal off, say, the kitchen and living room. Install a bed or two, or roll out the sleeping bags, and camp in those two rooms. This may be an emergency, but, with luck and the right attitude, there could be some fun in it.

HEATING

The following are alternative means of heating your home, assuming that your gas supply (if you use gas) has been shut off *(see Section 20, Natural Gas)* and your hydro supply has been disrupted:

- **butane heater**
  Safe, reliable, user-friendly, and portable — an excellent choice, although not widely available. *(For recommended retailers, see Resources on our website, www.earthquakeprep.ca.)*

- **propane heater**
  Reliable, user-friendly, portable — and widely available.

- **kerosene heater**
  Current models come with automatic lighting and a range of safety features, including an automatic extinguisher if the heater is jarred or tipped. Choose between convection (all-around) and radiant (directional) heat. Kerosene is non-volatile and economical, but it does have a slight odour. *(For recommended retailers, see Resources on our website, www.earthquakeprep.ca.)*

As explained in detail on page 62, wood-burning stoves and fireplaces are not to be counted on following a major earthquake (although they may be ideal in any other kind of disaster situation).

The following options will take the edge off the cold in a confined space (such as a tent or a vehicle). They also provide light *(see Section 7, Lighting)*.

- **candle(s)-in-a-can**
  Virtually indestructible (unlike ordinary candles, which may break in an earthquake) and long-burning.

- **candle-in-a-jar**
  A less good choice than candles-in-a-can, because the glass jar is likely to break in a major quake.

- **regular candles**
  Ideally, your candles should be short and stubby. Candles are easily knocked over and they do cause fires. Consider stabilizing candles by duct-taping them to whatever you are standing them on or in, and choose long-burning, drip-free ones.

- **tea lights**
  Virtually indestructible, these should be a part of everyone's emergency supplies.

WARM BEDDING

Take stock of your bedding. Consider how comfortable you would be living in your damaged home for a couple of months in mid-winter with little or no heating. Be prepared for a brief return to the days when a lot of folks went to bed dressed in everything but their parkas, or perhaps including their parkas. Wearing a toque or other hat to bed would be an excellent way to maintain body heat.

WARM CLOTHING AND OTHER OPTIONS

You probably already have all of the winter and outdoor clothing that you normally need, but you would be wise to consider additional means of keeping warm and dry following a major earthquake. Ideally, one or more of the following should be packed in each of your grab-and-go bags — the bags that you should have ready to grab if you need to leave home, work, or your vehicle in a hurry *(see Section 15, Grab-and-go Bags)*.

Look for these items in your nearest wilderness outfitters or camping equipment store *(for recommended retailers, see Resources on our website, www.earthquakeprep.ca)*.

- **sleeping bags**
  Portable and versatile. You can use a sleeping bag in almost any sheltered spot — even in damp conditions, if you have a groundsheet or tarp to place it on, or a lightweight survival bag to enclose it in. You can also use a sleeping bag with other bedding.

- **ponchos**
  These come in numerous weights and qualities. Coghlan's make an extremely lightweight, plastic, re-usable, hooded, emergency

poncho that (unopened) will fit into any pocket.

- **space blankets**
  There are numerous versions of these lightweight, thermal blankets, which are quite unlike the comfortable blankets you may sleep under at home. Space blankets all share the same objective, which is to use NASA/space-related, high-tensile materials to reflect (and in so doing capture) body heat, while offering protection from weather extremes. The Mylar blanket is probably the most compact, a 213 cm x 163 cm (84" x 64") sheet of extremely flexible, almost indestructible silver foil. In its original, unopened state, it will fit into a small pocket.

- **survival bags**
  These are made of similar material to space blankets *(see above)*, but are enclosed on three sides. Typically, they measure about 213 cm x 91 cm (84" x 36") and weigh about 74 g (2.6 oz).

- **Extreme Survivor suits**
  Step into one of these lightweight, highly visible international-orange, thermal coveralls, seal the velcro flaps and only your face and hands will be left exposed. Constructed of windproof and waterproof aluminized polyethylene film with heat-sealed seams, these Department of Trade/Canadian Coast Guard approved suits are designed to reduce the loss of vital body heat and the risk of hypothermia. Unlike space blankets and survival bags, they permit ease of movement, with no more than faces and hands exposed to the elements. If you plan to move around, however, remove shoes or boots before donning the suit and then replace your footwear — otherwise, the thin soles of the suit will rapidly wear out. Not suitable for strenuous exercise, because the fabric doesn't allow for evaporation, but ideal for use in an unheated or poorly heated home in the aftermath of the Big One, as well as in the great outdoors. Weight: 180 g (6 oz). Package size: 140 mm wide x 197 mm long x 19 mm thick (5 1/2" wide x 7 3/4" long x 3/4" thick). One size fits most. Price: about $27.00 Cdn.

- **tents**
  These come in any size you like, from a rudimentary, inexpensive, one-person, polyethylene tube tent, providing minimal shelter for one person but light enough to go in a grab-and-go bag, to spacious spreads of canvas that could, if necessary, provide a whole family with alternative accommodation. A tent should have a fly which protects its entire outer surface, and a built-in groundsheet.

Space blankets, survival bags, Extreme Survivor suits, lightweight sleeping bags, and tube tents are all, because of their compactness, ideal in different ways for grab-and-go bags *(see Section 15, Grab-and-go Bags)*.

TIP: An advantage of camping out in your yard over crowding into an emergency shelter is that you will be in your own space and able to watch over your home.

AWAY FROM HOME

It is early evening in the middle of January when the Big One hits. You are coming out of a movie, the mall, the ice rink, or wherever. For a number of endless, terrifying minutes you are engulfed in total chaos and confusion. Everyone around you is badly shaken, scared out of their wits. Some are stampeding. A few are seriously hurt; one or two may be dead. You have been cut by flying glass. Dazed, you try to assess your situation.

One thing is already clear — you are becoming extremely cold. When you left home, it didn't cross your mind that you might need a coat, scarf, gloves, or hat. After all, you were going from one warm place to another by car. You knew exactly what the trip looked like.

Things have changed. The back of your vehicle has been crushed by a collapsed wall; it's going nowhere else tonight. You think of squeezing into the front and running the engine for a while to warm yourself up, but the needle is on empty — you were going to top up the tank tomorrow. It is only a forty-five minute walk home — in broad daylight, that is, with no obstructions in the way — but you're not at all sure that you'll be able to make it in the freezing rain and in near-total darkness.

It doesn't matter what the story is. You (and whoever may be with you) are separated from the the warmth that we all take for granted. You have been caught unprepared, just like everyone else around you.

The story could have been different. Always have warm clothing on you, with you, or readily available whenever you're out — even in the height of summer. That may seem silly, over the top, and it will be — until you need it.

TIP: To protect yourself from extreme cold, wear multiple layers of clothing. Much of your body's heat is lost through the head and neck, which is why a hat and scarf can be essential. Bear in mind that wool retains a measure of heat even when wet, which is why wool sweaters, pants, and socks can be such a blessing in adverse conditions. Wet cotton kills.

On one of my earliest visits to BC, in the late 1970s, I was on a 14-day Educo (Outward Bound-type) adventure course that included whitewater canoeing. That canoes would capsize was a given: they all had buoyancy bags and everyone on the expedition was trained in canoe over canoe rescue. Equally important: we were all outfitted in army surplus clothing — made of, guess what, wool!

One of the things we learned was that there was no point in resisting the river (a symbol for life). The only hope of getting through the rapids (a symbol for life's challenges) without tipping was to go for them vigorously, head-on — and enjoy the ride.

HEAT AND WARMTH CHECKLIST

This checklist is for heating and warmth in your home. Your needs for heating and warmth in your workplace and vehicle, and for warmth while you are dependent on your grab-and-go bag, are looked at in those checklists. Remember: you won't need all of the items in this list. Just check and implement the ones that meet your needs.

MEANS OF HEATING

_____ x **wood-burning stove** ☐

_____ x **wood-burning fireplace** ☐

_____ x **butane heater** ☐
(to be used with adequate ventilation)

_____ x **propane heater** ☐
(to be used only in well-ventilated areas)

_____ x **kerosene heater** ☐
(to be used only in well-ventilated areas)

_____ x **candle(s)-in-a-can** ☐
(for emergency lighting as well as minimal heat) *(see also Section 7, Lighting)*

_____ x **regular candles** ☐
(for emergency lighting as well as minimal heat) *(see also Section 7, Lighting)*

_____ x **tea lights** ☐
(for emergency lighting as well as minimal heat) *(see also Section 7, Lighting)*

FUEL AND SUNDRIES

adequate kindling and seasoned wood ☐
(____ days continuous burning)

flue or chimney recently checked and free of obstructions ☐

_____ x **butane canisters (____g/____oz)** ☐
(storage location: _____)
(see also Section 6, Cooking and Section 7, Lighting)

_____ x **propane canisters (____g/____oz)** ☐
(storage location: _____)

_____ x **kerosene fuel** ☐
(amount:_____) (storage location: _____)

_____ x **paraffin fuel** ☐
(amount:_____) (storage location: _____)

_____ x **roll (or folded sheets) of aluminum foil** ☐
(to place under dripping candles or tea lights)

_____ x **regular matches**
(lots of them, stored in waterproof containers)

_____ x **waterproof matches**

_____ x **wind and waterproof matches**

_____ x _____

_____ x _____

WARM BEDDING

_____ x _____

_____ x _____

_____ x _____

_____ x _____

_____ x **sleeping bag**
(can be used under regular bedding for extra warmth) *(see also Section 13, Workplaces; Section 14, Vehicles; and Section 15, Grab-and-go Bags)*

WARM CLOTHING

_____ x _____

_____ x _____

_____ x _____

OTHER OPTIONS

_____ x **poncho**
(see also Section 13, Workplaces; Section 14, Vehicles; and Section 15, Grab-and-go Bags)

_____ x **space blanket**
(see also Section 13, Workplaces; Section 14, Vehicles; and Section 15, Grab-and-go Bags)

_____ x **survival bag**
(see also Section 13, Workplaces; Section 14, Vehicles; and Section 15, Grab-and-go Bags)

_____ x **Extreme Survivor suit**
(see also Section 13, Workplaces; Section 14, Vehicles; and Section 15, Grab-and-go Bags)

_____ x **tent** _____

_____ x _____

_____ x _____

Oₙₑ ᴏғ ᴛʜᴇ ᴍᴏsᴛ ᴜɴᴄᴏᴍғᴏʀᴛᴀʙʟᴇ aspects of the days following a major earthquake will be the lack of toilet facilities (ask any quake survivor). Poor sanitation and poor hygiene can rapidly lead to health problems such as dysentery.

In areas hardest hit by a major earthquake, assume that all sewer lines will have been damaged. They may or may not have been broken, but you will have no means of knowing. Do not flush toilets! If you do, raw sewage is likely to find its way into the open and cause contamination, which could be disastrous — for you and others.

Another reason for not flushing is that you may be grateful for the water in toilet tanks as part of your emergency water reserve (*see Section 4, Water*).

THE CAMOSUN COMMODE

This is my name for a simple and reasonably comfortable alternative toilet. Remove any water remaining in the toilet bowl and place an inverted plate in the bottom of the bowl. Lower the toilet seat. Place a kitchen garbage bag (approx. 56 cm x 60 cm / 22" x 24") inside the bowl and spread its top over the seat (so that you'd be sitting on the garbage bag) and attach it more or less permanently to the seat with duct tape. Next, place another garbage bag inside the first (as a removable/disposable liner) and attach it also to the seat with small pieces of duct tape. The first garbage bag is in case the second one rips: the plate in the bowl is to distribute the weight of the contents.

Ideally, you will urinate in one place (outside, if appropriate, or in another Camosun commode, which could be constructed on a suitably sized bucket or pail if there is no other toilet available) and defecate in another. It will make for easier and safer disposal if they are kept separate. A sprinkling of baking soda and a folded sheet of newspaper placed over defecation will help reduce odours and improve the aesthetics.

Partially filled liner bags should be removed as often as necessary, sealed, and then stored in larger outdoor garbage bags in a secure place (including a balcony).

ACKNOWLEDGEMENT: These instructions are based on a vivid description in *The Nitty Gritty of Personal Y2K "Insurance"* by Alex Tilley, founder and president of Tilley Endurables Inc.

OTHER OPTIONS If you already have a chemical toilet, you might choose to use it with plastic liner bags instead of the usual chemicals and holding tank. In normal times, the contents of the holding tank are emptied into a regular toilet and flushed away. This disposal method will not be available to you in the aftermath of a major earthquake, and you will not have adequate means of cleaning and sterilizing the tank.

There are portable models consisting of a lightweight, contoured seat supported on a sturdy, fold-flat, steel frame, with a disposable bag suspended below the seat. One of these and the half dozen bags that come in the package should be part of every vehicle kit *(see Section 14, Vehicles, and for retailers, see Resources on our website, www.earthquakeprep.ca)*.

You might want to think about ways of creating privacy for anyone using the toilet in exposed circumstances. One possibility would be to arrange bamboo poles around the toilet, tie a string across the tops of the poles, and place a blanket over the string.

HYGIENE You should have most, or all, of the following in your emergency supplies — in your home, and in all of your grab-and-go bags *(see Section 15, Grab-and-go Bags)*.

- **waterless disinfectant**
  This is available from most pharmacies and grocery stores. Simply put a thumbnail size amount on your palm and rub your hands together briskly until dry. It kills bacteria in a few seconds, without water or towels.

- **Benzalkonium chloride antiseptic wipes**
  These have the advantage of being extremely light and portable *(for suppliers, look under "Medical Equipment & Supplies" in your SuperPages)*.

- **general disinfectant**
  You can easily make your own disinfectant by mixing one part liquid chlorine bleach to ten parts water. Do not use granular household bleach, because it is poisonous.

- **examination gloves**
  You can buy these in boxes of 100 from your pharmacy. You may need different sized gloves for different members of your household. (Note: latex can cause allergic reactions.)

- **rubber household workgloves**

- **deodorizer**
  For an easy deodorizer, use baking soda. It stores well, absorbs odours, and is great as an extinguisher of small fires.

- **paper towels**

Human waste should be double or triple-bagged, labeled "human waste," and safely stored until the public is told where to take their garbage for burial, incineration, or removal to another location. Kitchen garbage bags and larger plastic bags will be among the most valuable items in your emergency supplies. Have masses of them. In the unlikely event of your having too many, they will be prime give-away and barter items.

WASTE DISPOSAL

You have been forewarned about the human waste problem and, with good planning, will have your emergency sanitation needs nicely in place. It's when you are away from home that you will run into problems. Most people have given the matter no thought at all and one of the first things that they will want to do after the shock of the earthquake is eliminate. As they'll likely keep on eliminating in a world suddenly bereft of usable toilets, the sooner neighbourhoods construct reasonably conducive latrines, the less exposed we will all be to human waste and the inevitable risks of disease.

LATRINES

A basic latrine is a trench dug 60 cm - 80 cm (24" - 30") deep astride which the user squats. Not much fun, but there it is. The waste can be sprinkled with a thin covering of lime before the trench is eventually filled in with dirt. The same procedure, by the way, should be used when disposing of dead animals, but in this case the trench should be 90 cm - 120 cm (3' - 4') deep.

A more attractive model is a series of neat holes approximately 25 cm (10") in diameter and 20 cm (8") deep with an opened-up, watertight kitchen garbage bag (or similar) in each. The user squats above the bag with his or her feet resting on the open edges of the bag. This design can be refined with a plank footrest on each side of the row of holes.

Where digging is undesirable or not feasible and there are enough buckets to meet demand, simple Camosun commodes — buckets with kitchen garbage bags as liners, their tops folded over the tops of the buckets — work well.

> Many years ago, when I was on anti-terrorist operations in the jungle-clad hills of what is now the Malaysian peninsula, I and my men would camp for the night in whatever reasonably level spot we could find that was close to running water. As I attended to briefings and radioed details of our position back to base, one of my Gurkha orderly's tasks was to build me a "basha" — a rudimentary, picnic table-like bed made of saplings, with a ridge-pole-and-poncho roof designed to withstand the torrential overnight rain. Another of his tasks was to construct my latrine. The version that I always preferred was the "joystick" model — a hole dug exactly the right distance from a stout sapling onto which I could hold.

Whatever kinds of latrine are built, privacy, shelter, and lighting will be essential. So will be the highest possible standards of cleanliness and presentation, because the intention will be to have people use them rather than take their chances elsewhere. Men's and women's enclosures can easily be protected with blanket-and-cord sides (supported by corner posts or other suitable fixings), a tarp roof to prevent the place from becoming a mud bath, and clear "men" and "women" signs.

One of the more heroic volunteer roles will be maintaining latrines — ensuring that they are kept as clean and tidy as possible, providing a constant supply of watertight refuse bags, and ensuring that partially filled bags are safely stored in larger bags in a secure location.

With indiscriminate usage and the absence of normal washing facilities, latrines are far from ideal, but it is difficult to imagine the scale of contamination that will exist if no such arrangements are made.

SANITATION CHECKLIST

This checklist is for emergency sanitation in your home. Emergency sanitation needs in your workplace are covered in that checklist and emergency sanitation needs while away from home or work are covered in the vehicle and grab-and-go bag lists. Remember: you won't need all of the items in this checklist. Just check and implement the ones that meet your needs.

CAMOSUN COMMODE

_____ x **kitchen garbage bags (approx. 56 cm x 60 cm/22" x 24")** ☐

_____ x **duct tape** ☐

OTHER OPTIONS

_____ x **portable toilet seat, lid, pail, bags, and disinfectant pouches** ☐

_____ x **pail or bucket** ☐
(to be used with plastic liner bags)

_____ x **chemical toilet** ☐
(to be used with plastic liner bags)

_____ x **kitchen garbage bags (approx. 56 cm x 60 cm/22" x 24")** ☐

_____ x **duct tape** ☐
(for attaching tops of liner bags to seat, or for sealing used bags)

PLUS (FOR ANY OF THE ABOVE CHOICES)

_____ x **toilet paper** ☐
(lots — they'll be good to barter with)

_____ x **large outdoor garbage bags** ☐
(for safe containment of wastes until proper collection is resumed)

_____ x **waterless disinfectant** ☐

_____ x **antiseptic wipes** ☐
(at least 100 per person, in appropriate sizes — don't skimp on these)

_____ x **general disinfectant** ☐

_____ x **examination gloves** ☐
(lots of them, in appropriate sizes)

_____ x **rubber household workgloves** ☐

_____ x **deodorizer** ☐

_____ x **paper towels** ☐

_____ x **privacy screen or beach windshield** ☐

_____ x **newspapers** ☐

The following excerpts are from an article in *The Vancouver Sun* of March 5, 2001:

continued from page 72

Earthquakes of similar violence have been recorded on this side of the Pacific. One of history's greatest series of earthquakes, thought to have been magnitude 8.7, occurred between December 16, 1811, and February 7, 1812, right in the centre of the United States. Residents of New Madrid, Missouri, were thrown out of their beds... by shaking so violent it was felt over an area of more than 2.5 million square kilometres. Shocks were felt in Detroit, Boston and New Orleans. The Mississippi and Ohio Rivers flowed backwards as the ground was thrust up, later carving new riverbeds for themselves....

Could such a quake happen on the West Coast? One already has. The Alaskan earthquake that killed 131 people in 1964 and sent lethal tsunamis across the Pacific registered 9.2 on the Richter scale, similar in magnitude to the event believed to have occurred off the West Coast of Vancouver Island on January 27, 1700. Tsunami records from Japan and coastal field work my many scientists from universities and federal, state, and provincial geological surveys have uncovered overwhelming evidence of a series of magnitude 8 or greater earthquakes about 300 years ago.

If an earthquake of similar force to those which destroyed Lisbon, Tokyo or Tangshan were to occur in proximity to the dense urban conglomerates of Seattle and Vancouver, the "wake-up" call of last week wouldn't even begin to cover it. Damage might run as high as $10 billion, which is why the Insurance Bureau of Canada worries that the insurance industry might not even be able to meet all the potential claims were a catastrophic earthquake to occur in the heavily populated Lower Mainland and southern Vancouver Island.[17]

Y OU PROBABLY KNOW YOUR HOUSEHOLD'S toiletry and medication requirements better than anyone else. You will want to have in place the right amounts of all of the right things when the Big One (or any other major catastrophe) happens. In the aftermath of a major quake, there will be no popping around to your local pharmacy: it may be open to the skies, but it is unlikely to be open for business.

Have on hand a month's supply (or more) of everything that you regularly use, and rotate supplies as necessary *(see Section 27, Check-ups)*.

A MONTH'S SUPPLY

In your home, keep medications in one easily-recognized, secure spot, such as a cabinet or drawer with a catch that will stop the contents becoming scattered in the violent shaking *(see Section 12, Securing Your Home)*. Consider keeping a soft, cloth bag near your medications into which to scoop them if you need to abandon your home in a hurry. And make sure that they are clearly labeled and identified.

In your vehicle and workplace grab-and-go bags, keep whatever toiletries and medications you will need if disaster catches you away from home *(see Section 15, Grab-and-go Bags)*.

If there is any equipment, such as syringes, oxygen tanks, wheelchairs, walkers, or crutches on which you or others in your household rely, consider the implications of any of these being damaged or otherwise becoming inoperable as a result of a quake, or of your being separated from them. Be prepared!

TOILETRIES CHECKLIST

This checklist is for toiletry reserves for your home. Toiletry needs for your grab-and-go bag are covered in that checklist *(see Section 15, Grab-and-go Bags)*. Remember: you may not need all of the options listed below. Just check and implement the ones that feel right for you.

_____ x **toothbrush** ☐

_____ x **toothpaste** ☐
(for lightness, consider small or partly-used tubes)

_____ x **dental floss** ☐

_____ x **comb** ☐

_____ x **shampoo** ☐

_____ x **razor** ☐

_____ x **waterless shaving cream** ☐

_____ x **waterless soap or hand disinfectant** ☐

_____ x **antiseptic wipes** ☐
(see Section 9, Sanitation)

_____ x **pre-moistened wipes** ☐

_____ x **sanitary napkins or tampons** ☐

_____ x **tissues** ☐

_____ x **deodorant** ☐

_____ x **lip balm** ☐

_____ x **sunscreen** ☐

_____ x **mosquito repellent** ☐

_____ x _____ ☐

_____ x _____ ☐

_____ x _____ ☐

_____ x _____ ☐

_____ x _____ ☐

_____ x _____ ☐

_____ x _____ ☐

_____ x _____ ☐

_____ x _____ ☐

_____ x _____ ☐

_____ x _____ ☐

_____ x _____ ☐

MEDICATIONS CHECKLIST

This checklist is for toiletry reserves for your home. Toiletry needs for your grab-and-go bag are covered in that checklist *(see Section 15, Grab-and-go Bags)*.

NAME _____

_____ x _____ ☐

_____ x _____ ☐

_____ x _____ ☐

_____ x _____ ☐

_____ x _____ ☐

_____ x _____ ☐

NAME _____

_____ x _____ ☐

_____ x _____ ☐

_____ x _____ ☐

_____ x _____ ☐

_____ x _____ ☐

_____ x _____ ☐

NAME _____

_____ x _____ ☐

_____ x _____ ☐

_____ x _____ ☐

_____ x _____ ☐

_____ x _____ ☐

_____ x _____ ☐

NAME _____

_____ x _____ ☐

_____ x _____ ☐

_____ x _____ ☐

_____ x _____ ☐

_____ x _____ ☐

_____ x _____ ☐

The following is part of a letter from Malcolm Fox, a member of the Vancouver Urban Search and Rescue Team, printed in *The Vancouver Sun* of July 5, 2000:

In our five years of existence, we have continually struggled with both levels of government for funding and to obtain operational experience in real disasters....

The federal government has pulled almost all of its military presence out of BC. The first 24 hours are critical in a major disaster, but the military will take at least that long to arrive — with no rescue capability.

Recently, the Canadian government sent financial aid to several areas struck by major earthquakes. Why not send professionals capable of providing real rescue assistance? It would be nice to get experience before the Big One here.[18]

I IS VIRTUALLY CERTAIN THAT YOUR home will be damaged in a major earthquake and there is a real chance that it will be badly damaged. Most likely, there are going to be numerous emergency repair or construction jobs to be done, probably without the benefit of supplies from the local hardware store. With telephones not working, you will be unable to call your friendly handyman or plumber.

Consider the items in the checklist overleaf, making sure that you have dedicated reserves (that you don't use in ordinary times) of "consumable" items (such as dust masks, nails, screws, hooks, etc.) that may otherwise be missing when you need them most. Where possible, go for tools and safety gear that are CSA (Canadian Standards Association) approved and unlikely to let you down.

TOOLS CHECKLIST

_____ x **multi-head screwdriver** ☐

_____ x **pliers** ☐

_____ x **hammer** ☐

_____ x **sledgehammer** ☐

_____ x **small axe** ☐
(can be used as a hammer)

_____ x **multi-tool** ☐
(you may choose to have one or more of these in your grab-and-go bag)

_____ x **knife** ☐

_____ x **saw** ☐

_____ x **pocket chainsaw** ☐

_____ x **hacksaw** ☐

_____ x **(with extra blades)** ☐

_____ x **chainsaw** ☐
(caution: only if you know how to use and maintain one)

_____ x **fuel for chainsaw** ☐
(caution: must be stored safely)

_____ x **shovel** ☐

_____ x **broom** ☐

_____ x **assorted nails** ☐

_____ x **assorted screws** ☐

_____ x **heavy-duty screw eyes** ☐

_____ x **dust masks** ☐

_____ x **crowbar/pry bar/wrecking bar** ☐
(for levering jammed doors, etc. — these bars come in a wide range of sizes)

_____ x **hard hat** ☐

_____ x **reflective safety/traffic vest** ☐

_____ x **heavy-duty leather gloves** ☐
(a must for clearing debris)

_____ x **examination gloves** ☐
(for hygiene)

_____ x **rubber household workgloves** ☐

_____ x **clear heavy-gauge plastic sheeting (3 m x 30 m/10' x 100')** ☐
(for covering shattered windows, sealing off unheated areas, emergency shelter,
catching rain, etc.)

_____ x **staple gun** ☐
(for attaching plastic sheeting, etc.)

_____ x **spare staples** ☐

_____ x **tarps** ☐
(of different sizes, these should be in addition to the tarp
that you may use for water catchment — *see Section 4, Water*)

_____ **m/ft cord** ☐

_____ x **safety glasses** ☐

_____ x **crescent wrench or pipe wrench** ☐
(for shutting off a gas supply — *see Section 20, Natural Gas*)

_____ x **short length of rubber tubing or garden hose** ☐
(for siphoning water)

_____ x **"Caution" or "Do Not Enter" barricade tape (300 m/1000 ft)** ☐
(for cordoning off dangerous areas)

_____ x _____ ☐

_____ x _____ ☐

_____ x _____ ☐

_____ x _____ ☐

_____ x _____ ☐

_____ x _____ ☐

_____ x _____ ☐

_____ x _____ ☐

_____ x _____ ☐

_____ x _____ ☐

_____ x _____ ☐

_____ x _____ ☐

_____ x _____ ☐

_____ x _____ ☐

_____ x _____ ☐

_____ x _____ ☐

_____ x _____ ☐

If you are unprepared for a disaster, it can shatter your life. If you're prepared, you can tip the balance between being a victim or a survivor.

Victims believe that major disasters occur in someone else's neighbourhood. Victims don't plan for emergencies. So when a disaster strikes, victims are overwhelmed by stress, trauma and injury.

Survivors, on the other hand, expect the unexpected and plan for it. They know what to do in a crisis. So when a disaster strikes, survivors are in better control and can get back on their feet more quickly.

No community is equipped to handle all the demands of a catastrophe. Help your community by preparing yourself.

Canadian Red Cross

Section 12
SECURING YOUR HOME

D URING A MAJOR EARTHQUAKE, YOUR home is likely to receive the rattling of its life. There is nothing that you can do about that, but you can minimize the damage to the structure and its contents by thoroughly checking for weak spots and potential hazards.

Try to imagine what will happen during the extraordinarily violent shaking of a megaquake. Numerous homes will be dislodged from their foundations. Many will partially collapse, or otherwise become uninhabitable. The contents of almost every home in the devastated region will lie in tangled ruins. If your home isn't to become a disaster area, there are things to be done. Don't worry about what your neighbours aren't doing — do what you need to do.

SOUND ADVICE

An excellent 25-minute video produced by Canada Mortgage & Housing Corporation (CMHC) and the Provincial Emergency Program (PEP), *Is Your Home Earthquake Resistant? Improve Your Odds in the Big One!*, describes powerfully the threat facing southwestern British Columbia. It explains clearly what needs to be done around a home to make it earthquake resistant. One of the many important points that it makes is that a new home is not necessarily any safer than an older one.

This video is a "must-see" — for homeowners and for everyone who lives in a home. Many of the procedures outlined below are demonstrated in the video, which will be helpful to people undertaking seismic upgrading themselves, those having the work carried out by a contractor, and those wondering whether they need to do anything at all. View it — then view it again and again. Hold viewing evenings for your friends. *(Note: the BCAA at Home recommended contractors' service referred to in the video has been discontinued.)*

FURTHER ADVICE

Essential reading for anyone interested in the integrity of their home and its contents is CMHC's comprehensive manual, *Residential Guide to Earthquake Resistance*.

Here are some brief excerpts from the introduction to the manual:

Surprisingly, people living in areas of high seismic risks seldom appreciate the risks they face.... Earthquake damage usually results from the absence of elementary construction details....

Canadians living in earthquake-prone areas of the country spend almost $15 billion on renovations annually. If a small portion of those funds were used by homeowners to complete the most basic recommendations of this guide, thousands of houses slated for renovation work this year would be much more prepared to survive an earthquake.... The disruption and costs of upgrading are minor compared to the catastrophic costs of doing nothing.

You can buy the video for $19.95 Cdn (plus shipping and GST) and the manual for $39.95 Cdn (plus shipping and GST) from CMHC, 200-1111 West Georgia Street, Vancouver BC V6E 4S4, telephone 604 731-5733. Or you should be able to find both at your public library.

TYING THINGS DOWN

Only you can decide how protected you want to be. Many forms of damage or loss are serious (for example, a home leaving its foundations; a brick chimney falling through the roof and living room ceiling; a hot water tank going walkabout). Others may be relatively trivial. You might, for example, feel it absurd to strap your books into your bookshelves (although after a quake you will wish that you had, especially as there are discreet, strong, flexible straps specially designed for that purpose), but will probably see the point of securing appliances and heavy items of furniture and equipment. You might not want to replace all of your china and glassware with unbreakable plastic, but you will probably see the point of lining some of your cupboards with non-skid matting and fitting seismic touch-opening latches.

Whatever isn't secured will become an IFO (Identified Flying Object).

GETTING THE JOB DONE

If you feel uncertain about where to turn for professional advice and competent work to secure your home, here are some pointers:

- **Geologists, foundation engineers, and geotechnical engineers** are trained and licenced to evaluate soil conditions and recommend appropriate action.
- **Consulting structural engineers and architects** are trained to evaluate structures.
- **A contractor** can implement the detailed plans and specifications prepared by an architect or engineer.
- **Professional organizations** such as CMHC provide advice on selecting the above. Understand what is involved, what is being recommended, and what is being promised. Then make an informed decision.
- **Useful professionals** can also be found in the *SuperPages* under "Earthquake Preparedness."

Be warned: home contractors are not the people to turn to for informed, unbiased, structural advice. You would be well advised to spend the $60 to $120 an hour necessary for a two- to four-hour hazards inspection by a suitable architect or engineer. Once you have determined exactly what should be done, call in the right contractor or experienced handyman *(for tips on working with contractors, see the CHMC manual)*. If you're tempted to do structural work and securing of major appliances yourself, bear in mind that very few homeowners are up to doing these things effectively. Unless you really know what you're doing, leave it to the appropriate professionals.

Skim through the precautions below and see which apply to you — bearing in mind that the detailed instructions given may or may not be the right ones for your circumstances.

1. bolting your home securely to its foundations

STRUCTURE

A wood-frame home that is not secured to its concrete foundation will likely be dislodged during the violent shaking of a major earthquake. To remedy this:

- Using 12.7 mm (1/2") wood and masonry bits, drill holes through the wooden sill and into the concrete foundation —

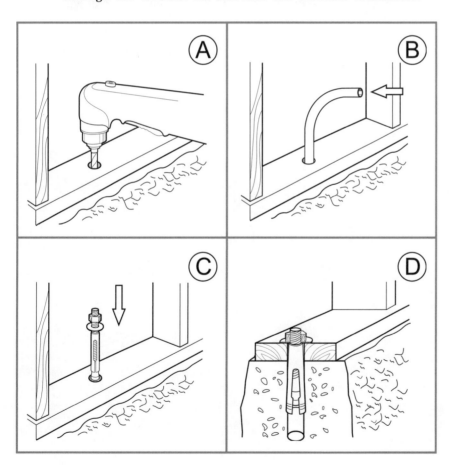

every 1.5 metres (4-6 feet) for a single-storey building and every metre (3-4 feet) for a two-storey or three-storey building. If space is tight, you may need to use a right angle drill (A).

- Blow the concrete powder out of the holes with a piece of 9.5 mm (3/8") flexible tubing (B) and hammer in expansion bolts 12.7 mm (1/2") in diameter and about 190 mm (7 1/2") in length (C).
- Tighten the nut on each expansion bolt (D).
- Additionally, use hold-downs and tension tie connectors (*illustrated below*) to increase the integrity of the structure.

2. **strengthening the cripple walls of your house**

Cripple walls are the short, wood-framed walls that extend from the top of the concrete foundation to the underside of the first (main) floor of the house. They are likely to be the walls of a "crawl space" or basement area. Laterally bracing these walls can greatly reduce earthquake damage. To do this:

- Nail 2" x 4" blocks of wood to the sill as needed (A).
- Secure the walls to the foundation using hold-downs (B) or tension tie connectors (C).
- Cut 12.7 mm (1/2") plywood to fit the inner side of the wall (D).
- Use a nail gun to fasten the plywood along all edges and to each stud with 75 mm (3") nails spaced 100 mm (4") apart (E). Be careful not to countersink the nails.

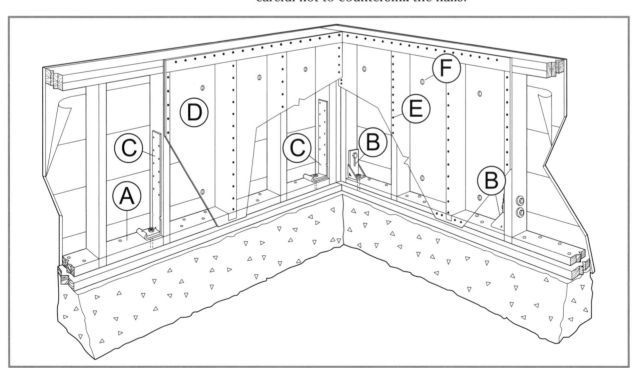

- Drill air vents through the plywood (F).

For a single-storey home, add plywood reinforcement to at least 30-50 per cent of each cripple wall and, for a two-storey home, reinforce at least 50-75 per cent of each wall. Bear in mind that just because your home is recently built doesn't mean it isn't vulnerable. There are presently no seismic code provisions for homes of less than four storeys or 280 square metres (3,000 square feet).

Peter Yanev, author of *Peace of Mind in Earthquake Country*,[19] estimates that as much as 70 per cent of all serious earthquake damage to older wood-frame houses would be eliminated by the upgrading of two basic conditions: the connection of the wood-frame system to the foundation and lateral bracing of the cripple walls.

3. **ensuring that the roof of your home is adequately attached to the rest of the house**
This is particularly important if the roof is tiled with clay, slate, or concrete tiles. A clay tile roof on a 150 square metre (1,600 square foot) house weighs about 7,800 kg (17,000 lbs) more than if the roof had asphalt shingles. The taller the house, the greater the hazard the roof load imposes. This is because the ground motion is amplified by the height of the building and weight of the roof, causing a much larger force to be applied to the supporting structural system.

TIP: Assess your neighbour's house, trees, and any other structures for possible risks to your property. A neighbour's falling chimney or tree could cause as much damage to your home as a falling chimney or tree of your own. A neighbour's home coming off its foundation could mean disaster for them and you.

4. **assessing whether your deck, porch, carport, garage, etc., are strong enough to withstand a major earthquake**
Now is the time to address these issues, all of which can be part of an architect's or an engineer's inspection.

5. **ensuring that your home is not at risk from falling chimney bricks, trees, utility poles, etc.**
Bracing or strengthening of chimneys in older homes may be necessary to prevent them from toppling. Brick chimneys may need to be replaced, and unstable and older trees and dead branches may need to be removed.

To prevent heavy debris from penetrating your ceilings, secure plywood or inexpensive, rough planks across the ceiling joists in your attic. Remember: whatever you use for this purpose will need to fit through your attic trapdoor or other access. Screw rather than nail them in place if that will be gentler on the ceiling below.

6. **placing invisible security film on some or all of your windows**
   Expect flying glass during a major earthquake. 4 mil - 7 mil security film will not prevent glass from shattering, but it will reduce or eliminate the risk of injury from shards of glass. And 10 mil - 14 mil film will make windows resistant to a determined break-in attempt (this is what banks have on their windows). This procedure is expensive, but consider how expensive the alternative might be — without protective film, you will probably face the nightmare of clearing up and disposing of masses of shards of glass. You will then need to cover the empty window frames with plastic sheeting *(see Section 11, Tools)*. *(Look under "Glass Tinting and Coating" in the SuperPages, or see Resources on our website, www.earthquake.ca.)*

UTILITIES

7. **securing your hot water tank**
   Your hot water tank (gas-fired or electric) should be firmly strapped to an adjoining wall, and possibly to the floor. This appliance can weigh over 180 kg (400 lbs) when full, and because of its height and weight, even moderate ground movement could topple it. A ricocheting water tank would cause chaos in your home and could inflict serious injuries. The broken gas or electrical lines would pose the risks of fire or electrocution; water from the broken water lines would flood your home in no time; and you could lose the 150-230 litres (40-60 gallons) of precious emergency water in the tank itself.

   Many emergency preparedness manuals and most plumbers' ideas of securing hot water tanks are inadequate. If the strapping used snaps or breaks free, you might as well not have bothered. *(For recommended strapping kits and installers, see Resources on our website, www.earthquakeprep.ca.)*

   To secure a hot water tank:
   - Wrap a 4 cm (1 1/2") wide, 16-gauge thick metal strap (A) around the water heater about 15 cm (6") down from the top, then bend and drill the ends in preparation for bolting together at the front of the tank (B).
   - Wrap a 4 cm (1 1/2") wide, 16-gauge thick metal strap (C) around the water heater about 45 cm (18") up from the bottom, then bend and drill the ends in preparation for bolting together at the front of the tank (D). This strap must be at least 10 cm (4") above the gas controls.
   - In the two steps above, some adjustment may be necessary to avoid water, gas, or electrical connections.
   - Take four lengths of EMT electrical conduit (E), each no longer than 75 cm (30"). Flatten approx. 4 cm (1 1/2") at one end of each conduit length. Drill the flattened ends and bolt them to the metal straps as shown (F). To do this, insert an 8 mm x

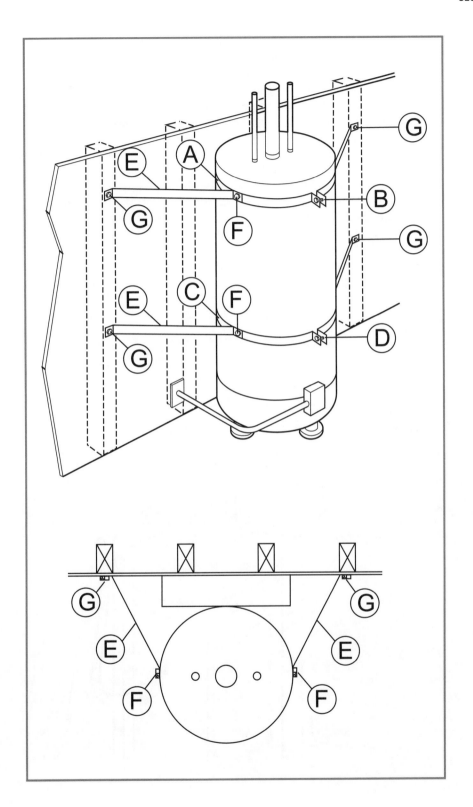

32 mm (5/16" x 1 1/4") bolt through the strap from the inside at the midpoint on each side of the water heater. Attach the drilled, flattened end of the conduit to the protruding bolt, add a washer and nut and tighten by hand.

- Bolt the ends of the upper strap (B) together and the ends of the lower strap (D) together, using in each case an 8 mm x 32 mm (5/16" x 1 1/4") bolt with washers.

- If the wall for attachment is wood frame, locate the studs in the wall on both sides of the tank.

- Flatten and drill the unattached ends of the four conduit lengths (G) where they meet an appropriate stud. Then bolt the flattened ends into the wall using an 8 mm x 76 mm (5/16" x 3") lag bolt for each fixing. Tap the lag screws gently into the holes to start them, then tighten with a wrench.

- For natural gas heaters, once the appliance has been secured, a flexible gas supply pipe may be installed. The installation of a flexible gas connection should only be carried out by a licenced

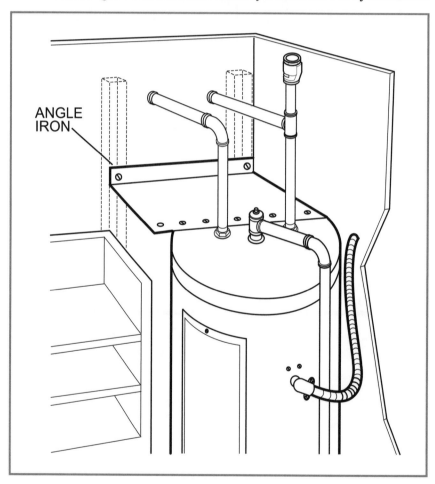

ANGLE IRON

gas fitter and will only be allowed if the hot water tank is effectively secured.

If bolting a tank to a concrete floor:

- Drill into the concrete, being careful to align the drilled holes with the holes in the tank. Place a lead expansion shield in each hole in the concrete and bolt the tank to the slab.

If bolting a tank to a concrete or masonry wall:

- Drill into the wall and place a lead expansion shield into each hole. Insert a 6mm (1/4") or thicker screw-eye into each shield. Brace the water heater with light steel cable wrapped around the tank.

ACKNOWLEDGEMENT: The above is a blend of the recommendations in the BC Gas flyer, *Domestic Natural Gas Water Heater Strapping, Conduit Method*, and CMHC's comprehensive manual, *Residential Guide to Earthquake Resistance*.

In a tight situation — when an electric water heater is located in the corner of a closet, for example, and shelving in the closet makes access to studs behind and beside the tank impossible — an inexpensive and effective procedure is to brace the tank with a piece of 5 cm x 25 cm x 60 cm (2" x 10" x 24") angle iron secured with suitable screws to the top of the tank and with lag bolts to studs that are accessible on a level with the top of the tank.

8. securing your furnace or boiler

In a major earthquake, furnaces, and boilers will topple, severing oil, gas, or electrical connections. If your furnace or boiler is not already bolted down, use the detailed instructions above for securing a hot water tank as guidelines.

9. securing your wood-burning stove

As explained in detail on page 62, the flue of a wood-burning stove may be sufficiently damaged in a major earthquake as to make the stove unusable, but the stove and flue should be secured ahead of time anyway — to reduce the chances of this happening, and to prevent the stove from sliding or toppling. If the stove topples while alight, there will be a high risk of cinders igniting your home. Anchor the stove to the floor and secure the pipe sections, being particularly careful that the seismic anchors and braces do not conduct heat from the stove to combustible materials in the house.

- **securing a stove resting on a brick hearth**

  Anchor each leg of the stove with a 10 mm (3/8") diameter bolt (A) through a 13 mm (1/2") hole in a new brick (B). Grout the new bricks to the existing hearth with 25 mm (1") of new grout (C). Alternatively, build a 20 cm (8") square brick pad (D) around each leg with a grout pocket (E). Fill the pockets completely with grout.

- **securing a stove resting on a concrete slab on grade**
  Anchor the stove directly to the concrete.

- **securing mobile home approved stoves**
  These units come with pre-drilled holes in the pedestals or legs and can be safely anchored to the underlying floor framing.

- **securing stove pipes**
  These should be anchored to the flue exit, and each of the stove pipe sections should be secured together using sheet metal screws (F). For double-walled pipe, make sure that the screws are short enough not to penetrate the inner pipe wall. If the stove pipe is unsupported for more than 2.5 metres (8 feet), provide one mid-height support by running the pipe through a factory-made attic radiation shield, using a pipe clamp (G) and two tension ties (H) to brace the pipe to a wall stud using 1cm (3/8") lag screws.

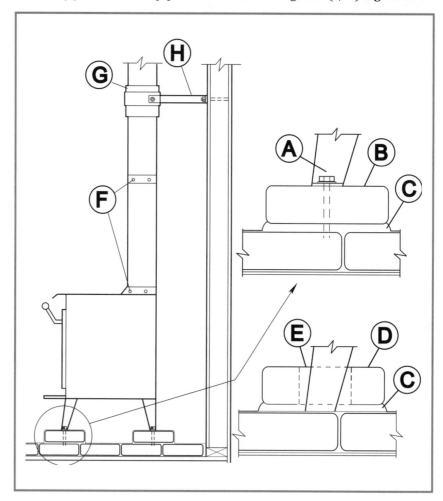

10. securing your above-ground propane tank

These tanks may move, slide, or topple during heavy ground shaking and are potentially dangerous unless both the tank and the pipes are properly secured. Gas leaks are frequently the cause of earthquake-related fires.

- Mount the tank on a continuous, 15 cm (6") thick concrete pad (A) and bolt the four legs to the pad using 13 mm (1/2") diameter bolts (B) with 8 cm (3") minimum embedded in the concrete.
- Install flexible hose connections (C) between the tank, the rigid supply line and entrance to the home.
- Clear the area of tall or heavy objects that might fall and rupture the tank or supply line.
- Keep a wrench tied on a cord near the shut-off valve and make sure that family members know how to use it.
- Make sure that you have a large fire extinguisher easily accessible and that all family members know how to use it.

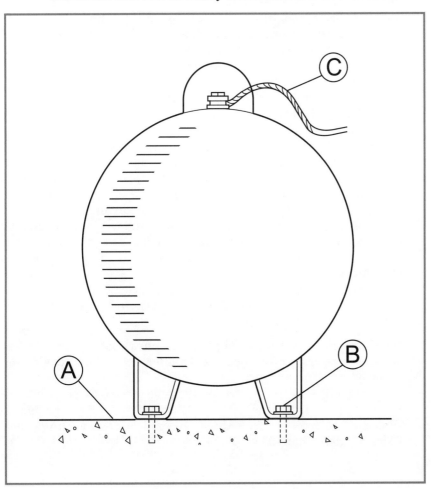

(For more information, consult your propane vendor and/or local fire department.)

APPLIANCES

11. securing your air conditioner

These heavy, bulky appliances can cause severe damage to a building and injury to people during an earthquake, especially where installed in windows, through walls, or on the exterior of a building.

The safest location for an air conditioner is at ground level outside a building, anchored to a concrete mat foundation. If located in a window or on a roof, it should be secured to the building in a manner that will successfully resist earthquake forces. Consult a structural engineer and the manufacturer's engineer for assistance.

12. securing refrigerators, stoves, washers, dryers, dishwashers, and other heavy appliances — and fitting longer, flexible gas connectors and electrical cords, where relevant, to allow for movement

Objectives: to prevent these appliances from crushing someone, blocking exits, or doing other damage, and to prevent rupturing of gas or electrical lines with the attendant risks of fire and explosion. This work should be undertaken only by a professional fitter.

Where possible, secure refrigerators, stoves, washers, dryers, and other appliances so that gas or electrical connections will not be ruptured. Refrigerators, because they are heavy and often top-heavy, are of particular concern. If mounted on glides (to facilitate cleaning) they can easily move. Lock the rollers on appliances that have them and place others on non-skid pads. Other restraints might include suitable lengths of steel cable or light metal chain secured at one end to the appliance (being careful not to damage the appliance) and at the other to a stud in the wall or to a suitable fixing point in the floor. The restraints should allow you to pull the appliance out for cleaning without over-extending the gas or electrical connection.

Another possible means of restraint is an adjustable nylon strap with an anchor loop or hook at each end. *(For retailers, see Resources on our website, www.earthquakeprep.ca.)*

13. securing your countertop appliances (ones that generate heat, such as toasters, coffee makers, countertop grills, and electric kettles)

This can be done by adding restraining edges to shelves and countertops, or by the use of Thumb Lock safety fasteners *(illustrated below)*, of which there are models designed to secure items weighing up to 90 kg (200 lbs).

14. **securing heavy furniture, top-heavy items, filing cabinets, grandfather clocks, etc**.

FURNITURE

Tall and/or heavy items such as bookcases, china cabinets, dressers, desks, filing cabinets, televisions, computers, and grandfather clocks present real hazards in an earthquake. Their potential for damage and injury may be lessened by a combination of placement and restraint.

The most potentially dangerous locations within rooms are those close to where occupants rest or work — for example, close to beds, sofas, easy chairs and desks — and where children play. Consider how each piece of furniture and other potentially lethal objects might fall or fly. Determine which items could block the path to an exit. Then consider re-arranging these items to avoid their becoming hazards.

One way to secure tall and/or heavy furniture is to use small steel angle brackets and lag bolts to connect the item to studs in the wall. Another is to use adjustable nylon straps with an anchor point or hook at each end — anchoring the ends securely to the wall. Yet

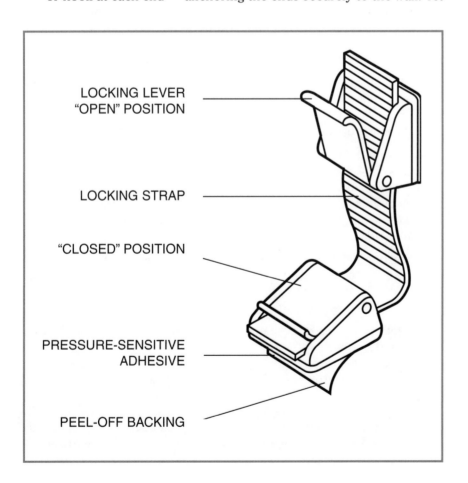

LOCKING LEVER
"OPEN" POSITION

LOCKING STRAP

"CLOSED" POSITION

PRESSURE-SENSITIVE
ADHESIVE

PEEL-OFF BACKING

another, ideal for computers, sound systems, and the like, is Thumb Lock safety fasteners, one of a number of specially designed restraining devices. *(For retailers of seismic restraints, see Resources on our website, www.earthquakeprep.ca.)*

15. **securing televisions, computers, sound systems, etc.**
Falling television sets apparently kill more children in earthquakes (in countries with an abundance of television sets) than any other cause. Use Thumb Lock fasteners, adjustable nylon straps, or quake-grade velcro, as appropriate, to secure appliances of this sort. *(For retailers of seismic restraints, see Resources on our website, www.earthquakeprep.ca.)*

BREAKABLES

16. **securing books (and loose shelves) from flying**
Books may be kept in place by a wooden dowel rail on the front edge of every shelf; or by plastic-coated curtain wire or high-tech stainless steel wire extended across the front of each shelf; or by flexible but strong, semi-invisible, purpose-made rubber bookshelf cord with quick-release hooks at each end. Bear in mind that loose shelves (the type that simply rest on four supports) will fly, along with their contents, unless restrained. *(For retailers of seismic restraints, see Resources on our website, www.earthquakeprep.ca.)*

17. **lining glass and china cabinets with non-skid matting**
You will find non-skid matting, packaged or by the roll, in hardware and fabric stores. It is inexpensive, readily available, and it may save some of your valuables in a moderate earthquake.

18. **securing lightweight ornaments**
Glass Tack and Quake Secure are two easy-to-use, easily-removed, putty-like fixatives. They may not be 100 per cent effective, but any reduction in broken glass and china will be a blessing. *(For retailers of seismic restraints, see Resources on our website, www.earthquakeprep.ca.)*

19. **securing pictures, paintings, wall decorations, and mirrors**
There are safety hangers designed to keep wall decorations on your walls. *(For retailers of seismic restraints, see Resources on our website, www.earthquakeprep.ca.)*

20. **installing strong safety latches on kitchen, bathroom, and other cabinet doors**
Imagine the entire contents of your cupboards strewn across your floors — a mixture of everything from jams, cereals, juices, and molasses to shampoo, toothpaste, and laundry detergent, clogged with coffee filters, tissues, tea towels, broken glass, and china. To prevent this, secure the doors of all cabinets and cupboards containing heavy, breakable, or precious objects. There are many

types of latches and catches available and they vary considerably in quality. You will need to choose between exterior-mounted (visible) and interior-mounted (invisible) ones. Your choices *(see overleaf)* include:

A. **hook-and-eye latches**
Exterior-mounted, these are effective only if secured at the time of the quake. Some come with a spring-loaded, child-resistant attachment.

B. **casement fasteners**
Exterior-mounted, these are effective only if secured at the time of the quake.

C. **table/sash locks**
Exterior-mounted, these are effective only if secured at the time of the quake.

D. **barrel bolts**
Exterior-mounted, these are effective only if secured at the time of the quake.

E. **push, touch, or pressure latches**
Interior-mounted, these are self-securing when the door is closed. Easily opened. These are difficult or impossible to find in local hardware stores. *(For retailers of these catches, see Resources on our website, www.earthquakeprep.ca.)*

E. **double latch**
Interior-mounted, these are less secure than push, touch, or pressure latches. Ideally, you will be able to adjust the tension on the ball-bearings.

RELOCATING

21. **moving large furniture away from exits**
Exits may otherwise become blocked.

22. **moving beds from beneath or beside unprotected windows**
Windows that have not been protected with security film will shatter in a major earthquake.

23. **relocating heavy and/or breakable objects to lower shelves**
The less distance they tumble, the less likely they are to be part of the debris littering your floors.

24. **removing pictures and hangings from above or near beds**
An unsecured wall decoration may be the first thing to wake you!

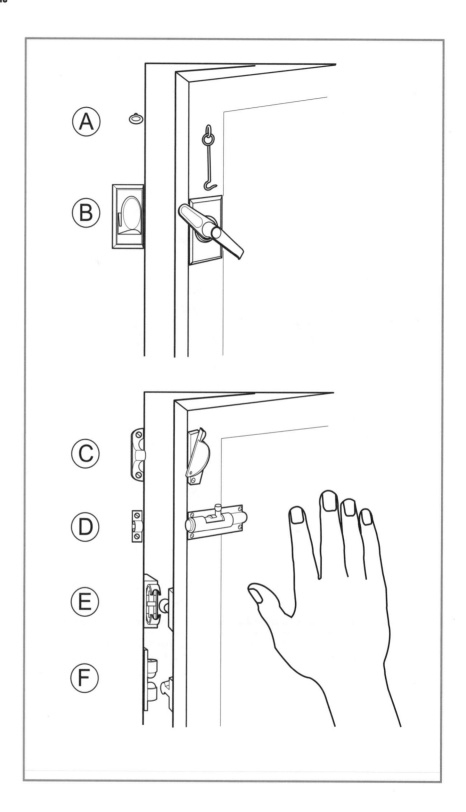

ACKNOWLEDGEMENT: The information above is adapted in part from CMHC's manual, *Residential Guide to Earthquake Resistance,* and from *On Shaky Ground* and *Living On Shaky Ground,* exceptionally helpful publications prepared by the Humboldt Earthquake Education Center, Humboldt State University, Arcata, California 95521-8299 in co-operation with other organizations and distributed, as a public service, by local newspapers.

SECURING YOUR HOME CHECKLIST

Remember: you won't need to implement all of the points in this checklist. Just check and implement the ones that are relevant for you.

1. Your home is securely bolted to its foundations ☐
2. The cripple walls of your house have been strengthened ☐
3. The roof of your home is adequately attached to the rest of the house ☐
4. The risks from falling chimney bricks, trees, utility poles, etc., have been addressed ☐
5. Your deck, porch, garage, etc., are strong enough (or have been strengthened) to withstand a major earthquake ☐
6. Invisible security film has been placed on some or all of your windows ☐
7. Your hot water tank has been secured ☐
8. Your furnace or boiler has been secured ☐
9. Your wood-burning stove has been secured ☐
10. Your above-ground propane tank has been secured ☐
11. Your refrigerators, stoves, washers, dryers, dishwashers, and other appliances have been secured — and fitted with longer, flexible gas connectors and electrical cords, where relevant ☐
12. Your air conditioner has been secured ☐
13. Your countertop appliances (ones that generate heat, such as toasters, coffee makers, countertop grills, and electric kettles) have been secured ☐
14. Your heavy furniture, top-heavy items, filing cabinets, have been secured ☐
15. Your televisions, computers, sound systems, etc., are secured ☐
16. Your books (and loose shelves) have been secured ☐
17. Your glass and china cabinets are lined with non-skid matting ☐
18. Your lightweight ornaments have been secured ☐
19. Your pictures, paintings, wall decorations, and mirrors have been secured ☐
20. Latches have been installed on relevant kitchen, bathroom, and other cabinet doors ☐
21. Large furniture has been moved away from exits ☐
22. Beds have been moved from beneath or beside unprotected windows ☐
23. Heavy and/or breakable objects have been relocated to lower shelves ☐
24. Pictures and hangings have been removed from above or near beds ☐

I F YOU SPEND AROUND FORTY HOURS A WEEK in a workplace that isn't your home, there is a one-in-four chance that a major earthquake will catch you there — separated perhaps by many kilometres from your family and your earthquake-prepared home.

Many of the risks and responses outlined in *Sections 2, During the Big One* and *Section 3, After the Big One*, will apply in your workplace. Filing cabinets and stacked boxes in the office will topple just as easily as china cabinets and hot water tanks in your home. Fragments of glass will cut just as badly and take just as many pairs of heavy-duty workgloves to clean up. And the actions and precautions to be taken during and immediately after the quake will be much the same.

STUCK

You have survived the horrific shaking of the quake unscathed, in large part because you knew exactly what to do and did it the moment the first shock wave hit. You and most of your colleagues have picked yourselves up and are facing the devastation as best you can. In the forefront of everyone's mind is getting home as soon as possible.

Try to imagine the hazards that you might face in retracing your morning commute. There is pandemonium everywhere. From your window you can see your car lying crushed under a large chunk of concrete. From the confusion outside you can guess that public transportation will be at a standstill. You have no idea whether the bridges between you and home are intact or lie submerged and impassable, because there's no sound from the office radio and television. It's winter, and by the time you and others have extricated and taken care of a partially buried colleague and given basic first aid to a number of others, it's pitch black outside. It's raining heavily: rain is coming through the gaping window frames. Hydro is out, the telephones are eerily silent, and the two office candles are almost burned down. You have a hard time picking your way through the mess of broken glass and strewn papers, around and over upturned desks and equipment. You're not the only one to realize that you will not be able to make it home safely tonight. Even in daylight tomorrow, your journey on foot may take many hours.

You're suddenly desperately hungry. You were in a lunchtime meeting and had time for only one sandwich. Now — although you probably don't know it — every food outlet in the vicinity is collapsed, closed, has already handed out whatever prepared food they had, or is being looted. Vending machines either aren't working or have already been broken into. The water cooler is wrecked, the water lines are broken, and the toilets aren't flushing.

This is unlikely to be an exact description of your situation, but whatever the picture is, you may need to spend the night in your workplace with colleagues who are frightened, emotional, possibly hurt, and just as concerned about their homes and loved ones as you are. Even if it isn't winter when the Big One strikes and it happens in the middle of a sunny morning and you are able to get in touch by cellphone with loved ones, there are plenty of things that you may be grateful for having in place.

SURVIVAL NEEDS

The checklist in this section relates to the likely needs of whomever may be in your workplace when disaster strikes. The provisions outlined are ones that any conscientious management team can put in place, easily and inexpensively. This may or may not be your responsibility, but it is most certainly in your best interest. For your personal needs once you leave the shelter of your workplace, you will need a grab-and-go bag *(see Section 15, Grab-and-go Bags)* — and you should encourage colleagues to have grab-and-go bags of their own.

SECURITY

The security of your workplace following a major earthquake will be your (or your management's) problem. Police protection will be minimal or non-existent; they will have far too many other things to handle. Some businesses and organizations have contracted private security firms to handle this kind of eventuality, but how effective these arrangements will be is anyone's guess.

Your workplace premises may be badly damaged and not easily protected. Plans need to be in place for securing whatever needs to be secured — everything from the physical structure (if that is important) to critical records, documents, and pieces of equipment. One of the few places that may be available for storing items with a degree of safety is the trunks of employees' vehicles.

EMERGENCY AND RECOVERY PLANS

A major earthquake will put thousands of businesses out of business forever and severely disrupt countless others. Many of those that survive will take years to return to normal. The toll in crippled and lost livelihoods will be incalculable.

The threat of a major earthquake is one of many reasons why businesses and organizations should have emergency and continuity/recovery plans in place. Emergency plans cover scenarios such as the one described above, where the safety and well-being of personnel are suddenly threatened and the securing of data, equipment, premises, and other aspects of the organization may be critical. Continuity/recovery plans cover everything that will ensure a return to normal operations as smoothly and rapidly as possible.

If your workplace has effective emergency plans, you will already be familiar with them — through your regular participation in emergency drills (which are not the same as fire drills). No drills — no effective plan. It's as simple as that. Continuity/ recovery plans are different: how much you know about them will probably depend on your role, but you should be confident that plans exist and that they are up-to-date.

One test of an effective continuity/recovery plan is how seamlessly a key employee could be replaced if he or she suddenly left or died. Most organizations count on that not happening, just as they count on the Big One not happening, at least any time soon. Every day, businesses and organizations are caught out as predictable but unanticipated things happen. One fateful day, thousands upon thousands of businesses will be caught out simultaneously. It'll be the day of the Big One.

If no effective plans are in place where you work, lobby for them, or initiate them. If you encounter resistance, don't be surprised: ostriches don't like to be disturbed while their heads are in the sand. But it's your and your colleagues' futures that may be at stake, so persist. Everyone deserves to know that their livelihood stands a chance of surviving a crisis and rebounding quickly. *(For referrals to emergency and business continuity/recovery consultants, see Resources on our website, www.earthquakeprep.ca.)*

WORKPLACE CHECKLIST

This checklist is designed to cover emergency supplies in up to four workplaces. These supplies should be in addition to those in workplace grab-and-go bags *(see Section 15, Grab-and-go Bags)*. Enter workplace names in the vertical boxes on the right. Remember: you are unlikely to need all of the options listed below. Just check and implement the ones that feel right for you.

FACTORY-BOTTLED WATER
Allow four litres per person per day (half for drinking, half for washing and cleaning)

small pack bottles (1 litre/34 oz)
small pack bottles (1.5 litre/51 oz)
small pack bottles (2 litre/68 oz)
small pack bottles (4 litre/135 oz)
bottle cooler bottles (11.3 litre/3-gal)
bottle cooler bottles (18.9 litre/5-gal)
water pouches (125 ml/4.2 oz)
(see Section 4, Water)

FOOD
self-heating meals
(see Section 5, Food)

WARMTH AND SHELTER
The following provisions may not make your workplace particularly comfortable in the aftermath of a major earthquake, but we're only looking at preparations for perhaps one night before everyone leaves for home.

butane heaters
(safe, if used with adequate ventilation; reliable and portable)
(see Section 8, Heat and Warmth, and Resources on our website, www.earthquakeprep.ca)

___g/___oz butane canisters
(a 227 g/8 oz canister lasts for about three hours, so eight such canisters
will provide 24 hours of continuous heat)

blankets
(allow two per person)

Mylar or space blankets
(lightweight, waterproof, windproof, flexible protection even in
sub-freezing temperatures: being reflective, they contain body heat:
allow one per person) *(see Section 8, Heat and Warmth)*

foam sleeping pads
(allow one per person)

clear heavy-gauge plastic sheeting (3 m x 30 m/10' x 100')
(for covering shattered windows, sealing off unheated areas,
emergency shelter, etc.)

candle(s)-in-a-can
(for warming confined spaces) *(see subsection Light, below; Section 7,
Lighting; and Section 8, Heat and Warmth)*

waterproof matches

wind and waterproof matches

LIGHT

regular flashlights

intrinsically safe flashlights
(see Section 7, Lighting)

electric lanterns
(see Section 7, Lighting)

spare batteries (size _____)

spare batteries (size _____)

hand-powered flashlights
(see Section 7, Lighting)

butane lanterns ☐ ☐ ☐ ☐
(to be used with adequate ventilation) *(see Section 7, Lighting)*

227 g/8 oz butane canisters ☐ ☐ ☐ ☐
(one canister will provide around five hours of continuous light)

wick lanterns ☐ ☐ ☐ ☐

containers of lamp oil (size ____) ☐ ☐ ☐ ☐

candle lanterns ☐ ☐ ☐ ☐

spare candles ☐ ☐ ☐ ☐

candle(s)-in-a-can ☐ ☐ ☐ ☐
(see subsection Warmth and Shelter, above; Section 7, Lighting; and Section 8, Heat and Warmth)

regular candles ☐ ☐ ☐ ☐

tea lights ☐ ☐ ☐ ☐

regular matches ☐ ☐ ☐ ☐
(stored in waterproof containers)

waterproof matches ☐ ☐ ☐ ☐

glow or lightsticks ☐ ☐ ☐ ☐
(see Section 7, Lighting)

☐ ☐ ☐ ☐
☐ ☐ ☐ ☐

HYGIENE/SANITATION

The water is off and you suspect the sewage lines may be broken. You are going to need alternative arrangements *(see Section 9, Sanitation for full details)*.

Camosun commode

kitchen garbage bags (approx. 56 cm x 60 cm/22" x 24") ☐ ☐ ☐ ☐
(at least six per person)

duct tape ☐ ☐ ☐ ☐

and/or

portable toilet ☐ ☐ ☐ ☐

kitchen garbage bags (approx. 56 cm x 60 cm/22" x 24") ☐ ☐ ☐ ☐
(at least six per person)

and/or

    chemical toilets ☐ ☐ ☐ ☐

    disinfectant ☐ ☐ ☐ ☐

plus (for all of the above choices)

    toilet paper ☐ ☐ ☐ ☐

    large outdoor garbage bags ☐ ☐ ☐ ☐
(for safe containment of wastes until proper collection is
resumed — and numerous other uses)

    general disinfectant ☐ ☐ ☐ ☐
(one formula is to add one part liquid chlorine bleach to ten parts water:
rinse thoroughly after use)

    examination gloves ☐ ☐ ☐ ☐
(lots of them, in appropriate sizes)

    rubber household workgloves ☐ ☐ ☐ ☐
(in appropriate sizes)

    antiseptic wipes ☐ ☐ ☐ ☐
(20 wipes for each person) *(see Section 9, Sanitation)*

    pre-moistened wipes ☐ ☐ ☐ ☐
(fine for freshening up, but remember they are not antiseptic)

    hand disinfectant ☐ ☐ ☐ ☐
(see Section 9, Sanitation)

    deodorizer ☐ ☐ ☐ ☐

    paper towels ☐ ☐ ☐ ☐

    privacy shelters ☐ ☐ ☐ ☐
(in case you need to set up toilet facilities in an exposed location)

☐ ☐ ☐ ☐

☐ ☐ ☐ ☐

☐ ☐ ☐ ☐

RESCUE/SURVIVAL/SECURITY

You may need any of the following for rescue work, making the premises habitable for the next 24 hours, or securing the premises against subsequent break-ins.

tarps

cord
(for securing tarps and similar purposes)

strong outdoor garbage bags
(for bagging debris, protecting or removing documents, etc.)

heavy-duty workgloves
(in appropriate sizes, for moving obstructions and debris)

hard hats
(in appropriate sizes)

dust masks

crowbars, pry bars, or wrecking bars
(for levering jammed doors, debris, etc.)

shovels

safety glasses

multi-head screwdrivers

pliers

hammers

sledgehammers

small axes
(can be used as a hammer)

saws

hacksaws
(with extra blades)

plywood sheets
(for securing broken windows, doorways, etc.)

assorted nails

assorted screws

heavy-duty screw eyes

clear heavy-gauge plastic sheeting (3 m x 30 m/10' x 100')
(for covering shattered windows, sealing off unheated areas, emergency shelter, catching rain, etc.)

staple guns
(for attaching plastic protective sheeting, etc.)

☐ ☐ ☐ ☐

spare staples

☐ ☐ ☐ ☐

short lengths of rubber tubing or garden hose
(for siphoning water)

☐ ☐ ☐ ☐

multi-use siphon pumps
(for siphoning gasoline — for example, from a stranded vehicle
to a driveable one)

☐ ☐ ☐ ☐

"Caution" or "Do Not Enter" barricade tape (300 m/1000 ft)
(for cordoning off dangerous areas)

☐ ☐ ☐ ☐

☐ ☐ ☐ ☐

☐ ☐ ☐ ☐

COMMUNICATIONS

two-way radios
(see Section 22, Communications)

☐ ☐ ☐ ☐

megaphones
(see Section 22, Communications)

☐ ☐ ☐ ☐

battery-operated strobe lights
(see Section 22, Communications)

☐ ☐ ☐ ☐

whistles
(see Section 22, Communications)

☐ ☐ ☐ ☐

glow or lightsticks
(see Section 7, Lighting)

☐ ☐ ☐ ☐

☐ ☐ ☐ ☐

☐ ☐ ☐ ☐

MISCELLANEOUS

battery-operated portable radios
(for picking up emergency broadcasts) *(see Section 22, Communications)*

☐ ☐ ☐ ☐

first aid kits
(see Section 16, First Aid)

☐ ☐ ☐ ☐

cash (small notes) □ □ □ □
(see Section 25, Smart Tips)

cash (rolls of quarters) □ □ □ □
(see Section 22, Communications and Section 25, Smart Tips)

inventories □ □ □ □
(instant reminders of what is stored in each workplace)

□ □ □ □

□ □ □ □

FIRST AID AND EMERGENCY TRAINING

lists drawn up of employees with recent first aid training □ □ □ □
(see Section 16, First Aid)

lists drawn up of employees with recent CPR training □ □ □ □
(see Section 16, First Aid)

□ □ □ □

□ □ □ □

WORKPLACES REVIEW

EMERGENCY PLANS

your workplace has full-scale earthquake/disaster/emergency □ □ □ □
plans in place, with drills at least twice per year

your workplace has some kind of earthquake/disaster/emergency □ □ □ □
plan in place, with drills at least twice per year

you and/or others have initiated such plans — in which you □ □ □ □
will be participating

BUSINESS RECOVERY PLANS

your workplace has full-scale business recovery plans in place □ □ □ □

your workplace has some kind of business recovery plan in place □ □ □ □

you and/or others have initiated such plans □ □ □ □

I F YOU USE A VEHICLE TO ANY EXTENT, there is a very real possibility that you will be on the road when a major earthquake hits and that blocked roads, or damage to your vehicle, will prevent you from driving farther. If that happens, your vehicle may suddenly become your only place of shelter and safety, your temporary life support capsule.

This section looks at what you might keep in your vehicle in addition to the contents of your vehicle grab-and-go bag *(see Section 15, Grab-and-Go Bags)*. If, for example, you have water, food, and other essentials as parts of your vehicle kit, there is a very good chance that your vehicle grab-and-go bag will be intact when you resume your journey — probably on foot.

I hope that you are in the habit (or that, as a result of reading this guide, you will develop the habit) of always wearing, or having with you, on any trip away from home clothing suitable for the conditions outside — even on the most local trips *(see Section 8, Heat and Warmth)*. Why? Because there are countless circumstances, earthquake-related and otherwise, in which you could become separated without warning from the shelter and warmth of your vehicle, or be cut off from your home, workplace, or other place of shelter and sustenance. If you can't be sure of having suitable outdoor clothing on you, or with you, whenever you go out, then include warm outerwear in your vehicle kit.

Here are items that you will need, or should consider, for your vehicle:

VEHICLE CHECKLIST

This checklist is for kits for up to three vehicles. The assumption is that you will also have one or more vehicle grab-and-go bags in any vehicle. Enter vehicle names in the vertical boxes on the right (for example, "Honda" or "minivan"). Remember: you are unlikely to need all of the options listed below. Just check and implement the ones that feel right for you.

BAGS

large tote bag
(to contain your vehicle kit)

FACTORY-BOTTLED WATER *(see Section 4, Water)*

small pack bottles (1 litre/34 oz)

small pack bottles (1.5 litre/51 oz)

small pack bottles (2 litre/68 oz)

small pack bottles (4 litre/135 oz)

bottle cooler bottles (11.3 litre/3 gal)

bottle cooler bottles (18.9 litre/5 gal)

water pouches (125 ml/4.2 oz)

HOME-CONTAINERIZED WATER *(see Section 4, Water)*

water packs (___ litres/___oz/gal each)

water packs (___ litres/___oz/gal each)

FOOD *(see Section 5, Food)*

self-heating meals

three-day emergency rations

SOS Millennium bars

canned foods (such as tuna, salmon, or sardines)

dried fruit or trail mix

hard candies

UTENSILS

    paper (disposable) plates/bowls   □ □ □

    plastic cutlery   □ □ □

    manual can opener with bottle opener   □ □ □

    □ □ □

    □ □ □

    □ □ □

CLOTHING, WARMTH, SHELTER *(see Section 8, Heat and Warmth)*

    rain gear   □ □ □

    warm jacket   □ □ □

    warm hat   □ □ □

    warm gloves   □ □ □

    warm socks   □ □ □

    sturdy shoes or boots   □ □ □

    reflective safety/traffic vest   □ □ □

    □ □ □

    □ □ □

WARMTH AND LIGHT *(see Section 8, Heat and Warmth and Section 7, Lighting)*

    blanket   □ □ □

    candle(s)-in-a-can   □ □ □

    regular matches   □ □ □

    waterproof matches   □ □ □

    wind and waterproof matches   □ □ □

    flashlight   □ □ □

    electric lantern   □ □ □

    spare batteries (size ____)   □ □ □

    □ □ □

    □ □ □

SANITATION *(see Section 9, Sanitation)*

    portable toilet

    homemade alternative

    (to be lined with kitchen garbage bags)

PLUS

    large kitchen garbage bags (approx. 56 cm x 60 cm/22" x 24")

    disinfectant

    toilet paper

    examination gloves

    rubber household workgloves

    antiseptic wipes
    (see Section 9, Sanitation)

    pre-moistened wipes

    small container of hand disinfectant

    small towels

    paper towels

    privacy screen or beach windshield

SURVIVAL

    heavy-duty leather gloves

    fire extinguisher
    (see Section 18, Fire)

    first aid kit
    (see Section 16, First Aid)

tow line ☐ ☐ ☐

booster cables ☐ ☐ ☐

spare alternator belt (fan belt) ☐ ☐ ☐

bag of sand or cat litter ☐ ☐ ☐
(for traction if stuck in mud, snow, etc.)

approved gas can (filled) ☐ ☐ ☐
(caution: ensure that this is safely stored)

multi-purpose pump ☐ ☐ ☐
(for siphoning gas from a stranded vehicle)

shovel ☐ ☐ ☐

folding saw ☐ ☐ ☐

strong string or cord ☐ ☐ ☐

compass ☐ ☐ ☐

maps ☐ ☐ ☐

cash (small notes) ☐ ☐ ☐
(see Section 25, Smart Tips)

cash (rolls of quarters) ☐ ☐ ☐
(see Section 25, Smart Tips)

☐ ☐ ☐

☐ ☐ ☐

☐ ☐ ☐

☐ ☐ ☐

☐ ☐ ☐

SIGNALLING/COMMUNICATION (see Section 22, Communications)

battery-operated strobe light ☐ ☐ ☐

glow or lightsticks ☐ ☐ ☐

whistle ☐ ☐ ☐

megaphone ☐ ☐ ☐

indelible marker pen ☐ ☐ ☐

note pad
(If you have to abandon your vehicle, leave a clearly legible note on the dash stating who you are — your name, address and telephone number — who is with you, where you are headed, when you might return for your vehicle, and anything else that may be helpful to emergency services or concerned members of the public. A note like this is unlikely to increase the chances of your vehicle being broken into — if someone is intent on breaking in, they will do so anyway — but it may prove helpful or even invaluable.)

pen

PET NEEDS *(see Section 21, Pets)*

water
(allow for pet needs in your own supplies — see above)

food

bowls
(for food and water)

MISCELLANEOUS

entertainment
(such as books, cards, and games and, for children, colouring books, crayons, and toys)

inventory
(an instant reminder of what is stored in each vehicle)

Y OU MAY NEED TO EVACUATE YOUR HOME, workplace, or vehicle at very short notice — possibly with no notice at all. It is for this eventuality that you and those close to you will each need one or more lightweight backpacks or tote bags with shoulder straps (in order to leave your hands as free as possible) containing essentials. If the packs or tote bags that you choose are not waterproof, pack the contents in well-sealed plastic bags.

Why might you need to abandon your home or workplace in a hurry? One possibility is that it will be on fire — you may have only seconds in which to get yourself and anyone else out, hopefully having time to seize your packs on the way. Another is that your home or workplace will be structurally unsafe or at risk from landslides, flooding, or a number of other possible hazards. You may be ordered out, with no prospect of returning for days, or months, or ever. Or you may need to reach a separated family member, friend, or relative.

Why might you abandon your vehicle? Most likely, because it's stuck, or the roads are impassable. It doesn't matter why: if you have to leave where you are in a hurry, you won't have time to hunt around for necessities. And it could be hours or days before you reach your next place of refuge.

You and every member of your household should have a grab-and-go bag:

- **at home**, in an easily accessible place

- **at work**, in an easily accessible but secure place

- **in each vehicle** that you regularly use

For example, if the whole family uses the minivan, you should each have a pack in the minivan. If only one of you regularly uses the Honda, then there should be a pack for that person in the Honda.

Each of you who goes out to work should have a workplace bag in your office or in your locker. If you regularly take a vehicle to work and park it in the open (where you will probably be able to reach it following a megaquake), you might choose to rely on your vehicle grab-and-go bag while at work — but, if you park underground or in some other vulnerable spot, don't count on being able to retrieve that bag.

Does this sound a bit elaborate, having a separate bag wherever you turn? Of course it does — but you won't want to be caught without one.

CONTENTS

Consider carefully what each bag should contain. For example, you are unlikely to want a thermal blanket, thermal bag, and thermal protective suit, although all three are included in the checklist. You may not want any of them.

WARM OUTER CLOTHING

So many of us go out in winter conditions dressed only in indoor clothes — trusting that the vehicle we're in will get us to our destination safe and warm. In normal circumstances, of course, it does, but if the Big One — or any disaster — catches us while we're away from home, the outcome could be anything from extremely uncomfortable to fatal *(see Section 17, Hypothermia).*

The answer is to have warm outer clothing on you, or with you, whenever you're away from home — exactly as you would if you were a sensibly equipped hiker venturing into a wilderness area. Just as no wilderness hiker can be sure of being back to civilization by nightfall, no one living in southwestern British Columbia can have any idea where they'll be — or how far from home — when a major earthquake hits.

"I can understand having warm clothing with me in the middle of winter," you might think, "but why should I have warm clothing with me when I head for the beach?" If the Big One hits while you're at the beach and it takes you 24 hours to make your way home through total chaos, you will be extremely glad of everything warm and sustaining that you may have with you.

Your wise choices are between:

- **always wearing, or having with you, warm enough clothing to see you through a long night in the open** — possibly in extremely adverse conditions.

- **having warm outer clothing permanently stashed in your vehicle and in your grab-and-go bag.**

Or you may settle for a compromise between these.

STURDY FOOTWEAR

As with clothing, so with footwear. Wherever you are when the Big One strikes — in a meeting, at a volleyball party, at a friend's barbecue, or cruising the mall — if you are wearing, or have with you, sturdy footwear, you won't be facing the long and hazardous hike home across debris-strewn terrain in your high heels, thin-soled loafers, or disintegrating rubber beach shoes.

INTACT AND AVAILABLE

Keep the contents of your grab-and-go bags intact at all times prior to an earthquake. Don't borrow from them. Store them, at home and at work, in places where (as far as you can possibly guess) they will be accessible to you following a quake. Remember, parts of buildings may collapse, doors may jam, etc.

The items on the following checklist are ones you should consider for your home, workplace, and vehicle grab-and-go bags.

Important: in your workplace and vehicle you should have additional supplies — supplies that you might draw on in your workplace or vehicle while leaving your grab-and-go bag intact for your long hike home *(see Section 13, Workplaces and Section 14, Vehicles).*

PETS

You are going to need one or more grab-and-go bags for any pets in your household. *(These needs are covered in Section 21, Pets.)*

READY-MADE GRAB-AND-GO BAGS: The risk is that you will buy a nice, "feel-good", ready-made pack and think that you are earthquake or emergency prepared — when you aren't. That said, you might want to look at what's available. These packs are usually cost-effective and could save you many hours of shopping around — but you will need to supplement them with personal items. *(For suppliers of ready-made grab-and-go bags, see Resources on our website, www.earthquakeprep.ca.)*

GRAB-AND-GO BAGS CHECKLIST

This checklist is for up to a dozen different people and/or locations. Enter names and/or locations in the vertical boxes on the right (e.g., "Dad/Work," "Billy/Home"). Remember: you won't need all of the items suggested. Just check and implement the ones that meet your needs. Go for compactness and lightness — and put a waterproof label on each pack.

BAGS

suitable tote bag or backpack

plastic bags
(for protecting contents of pack)

WATER *(see Section 4, Water)*

small pack bottles (1 litre/34 oz)

small pack bottles (1.5 litre/51 oz)

water pouches (125 ml/4.2 oz)

water bottle, canteen, or container of water

water filtration system

(other means of treating water)

FOOD *(see Section 5, Food)*

self-heating meals

three-day emergency rations

SOS Millennium bars

canned foods (such as stews, tuna, salmon, or sardines)

dried fruit or trail mix

hard candies

UTENSILS

manual can opener (with bottle opener)

plastic bowl

set of cutlery

WARMTH AND SHELTER
(see Section 8, Heat and Warmth)

warm outer clothing

rain garment or emergency poncho

sleeping bag
(lightweight)

emergency tube tent
(lightweight, rudimentary shelter)

thermal, space, or survival blanket

thermal, space, or survival bag

Extreme Survivor thermal protective suit

waterproof ground sheet or small tarp

emergency candle(s)-in-a-can

waterproof matches

wind and waterproof matches

change of clothing

LIGHT *(see Section 7, Lighting)*

regular flashlight

spare batteries
(packaged or plastic-wrapped)

spare bulbs

hand-powered flashlight

glow or lightsticks

SANITATION (*see Section 9, Sanitation*)

kitchen garbage bags
(approx. 56cm x 60cm/22" x 24")

toilet paper
(wrapped in plastic)

Coghlan's personal tissue rolls
(coreless, compact, 140 sheets per roll)

examination gloves

rubber household workgloves

antiseptic wipes
(100 wipes for each person)

pre-moistened wipes
(fine for freshening up, not antiseptic)

small container of hand disinfectant

TOILETRIES (*see Section 10, Toiletries and Medications*)

toothbrush

toothpaste

dental floss

comb

shampoo

razor

waterless shaving cream

waterless soap or hand disinfectant

pre-moistened wipes

sanitary napkins/tampons

tissues

deodorant

lip balm

sunscreen

mosquito repellent

MEDICATIONS *(see Section 10, Toiletries and Medications)*

SURVIVAL

heavy-duty leather gloves

personal first aid kit
(see Section 16, First Aid)

multi-tool

Swiss Army knife
(alternative to a multi-tool)

strong string or cord

whistle
(see Section 22, Communications)

indelible or permanent marker pen

small note pad

ballpoint pen

ziplock plastic bags

map of your area

compass

spare eyeglasses or contact lenses

cash (small notes)

cash (rolls of quarters)
(see Section 22, Communications)

ADDITIONAL TOOLS

folding saw

pocket commando chain saw

small axe
(can be used as a hammer)

collapsible shovel

small pry bar

duct tape

dust masks

protective glasses

small watertight container of baking soda
(for smothering fires)

FOR CHILDREN

entertainment
(such as books, cards, games, colouring books, crayons, and toys)

MISCELLANEOUS

laminated "disaster plan" card
(see Section 23, Documentation)

battery or wind-up radio
(see Section 22, Communications)

photocopies of vital documents
(see Section 23, Documentation)

photographs of immediate family
(helpful for identification)

photographs of any pets
(helpful for identification)

sun hat

tube of sunblock

UV sunglasses

inventory

The following excerpts are from *The Province's* two-day special of July 23-24, 2000 entitled "The Big One":

Here's what an 8.5 subduction earthquake could do to us based on a scenario by BC emergency officials. At 6:00 a.m., some 150 km off the BC coast at a depth of 40 km, one of the Earth's plates suddenly slips below another, creating a major earthquake.

The water level on the BC coast suddenly drops more than a metre and the ground shakes violently throughout the Lower Mainland and Vancouver Island for three to four minutes. Within minutes, five-metre-high tsunami waves surge one after the other on to the open shoreline of Vancouver Island.

West Coast of Vancouver Island

Partial wipe-out of Ucluelet, Tofino, Gold River, Tahsis and virtually every western Island settlement occurs.... A significant tourist population in the area's National Parks and all park staff and records vanish. All major roads into the area are washed out and road access ends at the tsunami high-water mark, generally two to three kilometres outside of town.

The waves are channelled up Port Alberni inlet and strike hard. The harbour and the channel are choked with debris and the industrial area and older downtown core suffer major damage.... Port Renfrew, the closest community to the epicentre, is essentially at sea level and will be destroyed. Some residents may survive, but they will be few and require evacuation.[20]

Continued on page 172

I N NORMAL CIRCUMSTANCES, IF YOU FIND yourself at the scene of an accident or confronted by a medical emergency, you know that help is only a telephone call away. In an urban setting, you will only have to render assistance for a few minutes, in whatever ways you can, if you can, before you hear the sounds of approaching sirens and the problem is taken care of by experts. In a rural setting, help may take a little longer to arrive.

Even in the most dramatic circumstances, such as the Oklahoma bombing of April 19, 1995, the Quebec ice storm of January 1998, or the Twin Towers carnage of September 11, 2001, help pours in rapidly from all quarters. Emergency services, military, and every other imaginable form of assistance is on the spot, if not within minutes, then within very few hours. Equipment and personnel are rushed in, hospitals mobilize to receive the injured, the dead are handled, the traumatized are counselled, the situation is cleared up, and things return to a semblance of normality in relatively short order.

Following a major earthquake, it will be different. The outside world will be racing to help, for sure, but the scale of the devastation, the difficulties of access, and insufficient and inadequate equipment will make that response seem pretty impotent for a while. Rescuers — emergency services and volunteers — will be overwhelmed. Their first priority (apart from staying operational themselves) will be saving lives — searching for and recovering survivors, and tending to the most seriously wounded — while attempting to put out fires and handle the general chaos surrounding them. It will be days before adequate reinforcements arrive and less serious situations can be tackled.

As Stephen Hume put it in *The Vancouver Sun* on June 6, 1998:

> And just about now you discover that your kids have been seriously cut by flying glass. What are you going to do? The hospital, also in darkness, partly rubble, lies on the far side of a bridge. The bridge is intact, but its approaches no longer exist. And you couldn't get to the bridge anyway because overpasses have pancaked into the roads below.
>
> Do you know how to staunch your kid's bleeding? Do you know what to do for a severe concussion? For bones broken by a cannonading drawer? If you don't, who is going to help you? The answer, of course, is probably nobody.[21]

You may be faced with anything from relatively minor injuries to horrific ones (dealing with a crushed or severed limb, for example); from medical emergencies (a stroke victim, or a diabetic about to go into a coma) to dead bodies, with nothing more than the knowledge and equipment that you and shocked, distraught neighbours or onlookers can scrape together. No one is expecting you to become a paramedic or fully trained emergency room doctor overnight but, if your knowledge and experience are as minimal as most people's are, you're likely to feel inadequate and desperate when the time comes.

> Faced with possibly horrendous injuries in the aftermath of the Big One, you would give your eye teeth to know what to do and have the means to do it. Most of the people around you will be next to useless — helpful and concerned, but ill-informed and ill-equipped. Why? Because they never took the time to become trained in first aid — or, if they did, they have long since forgotten everything they learned. After all, there were always paramedics and medical professionals to handle these things. Well, now there aren't, and the screaming of that person who is going to bleed to death in the next few minutes if the right things aren't done may be your problem.

FIRST AID TRAINING

If you are not thoroughly familiar with First Aid and CPR (cardio-pulmonary resuscitation) — if you couldn't confidently take charge of an emergency situation, knowing how to deal with bleeding, both external and internal, burns, breathing difficulties, cardiovascular emergencies, unconsciousness, choking, eye injuries, and much else — now is the time to take or retake a first aid class. Call St John Ambulance or the Canadian Red Cross *(see your SuperPages or page 265 of this guide)*.

There is no telling when such knowledge might save someone's life — and save you from blaming yourself for not knowing what to do.

DISASTER SCENE MANAGEMENT

Ideally, in a disaster situation, someone who is uninjured and relatively unaffected by what has happened will take overall charge of the situation, and others will respond by taking responsibility for other aspects of what needs to be done.

The first step in disaster scene management is to evaluate the situation. Take however many moments may be required to determine what the best course of action is for everyone involved. If possible, call for help and make sure that persons with suspected head or spinal injuries are not moved. In the aftermath of a major earthquake, a priority for many rescuers will be to assess the possibility of further structural collapses before attempting to extricate victims and risking being injured or buried themselves. For example, a rescuer's smartest move might be to race to obtain heavy workgloves and tools that will make a rescue effort truly effective, rather than a further-bloodied fiasco.

Rescuers are valuable only as long as they themselves remain functional. If they become incapacitated for any reason, they compound the disaster.

Triage — the sorting of casualties according to priority — may be a vital part of the overall assessment process. In triage, you are seeking to achieve the greatest possible good for the greatest number of those whose lives and welfare are at stake. It recognizes that you, and whoever may be working with you, will be unable to provide optimum care for everyone simultaneously.

TRIAGE

Your order of priorities will be:

- **priority #1 — trauma cases, those in need of immediate, life-saving intervention who can be saved with prompt attention**
  This may include casualties in imminent danger of dying through loss of blood, or a victim whose airway can be re-established by, for example, re-positioning their head or lifting the beam that is trapping and suffocating them.

  The normal procedure with trauma cases is to first check the victim's airway and breathing. For someone who is unconscious, you need to open the airway and, if breathing is absent, give artificial respiration. In the absence of a pulse, you might start CPR. Under normal circumstances, any other treatment is secondary to maintaining respiratory and cardio functions, because a victim who is not breathing is either on the verge of dying, or dead.

  With breathing stabilized, you would check for and handle other life-threatening conditions — instructing a bystander (if there is one) to provide manual support for the casualty's head and neck if head or spinal injuries are suspected. You would stem any severe bleeding by applying direct pressure at the bleeding site, followed by whatever level of dressing you can provide, and then move into treatment for shock.

  Things are likely to be different in the aftermath of a megaquake. In a triage situation, where intervention is desperately required for a number of victims and there is little hope of professional help arriving, someone with no carotid pulse may have to be regarded as beyond your help. CPR is only practicable if followed within minutes by advanced cardiac life support and admission to the emergency ward of a hospital — and, after a major earthquake, that level of support is unlikely to be available to you. There may, however, be other lives that you can save.

- **priority #2 — serious casualties who will survive while you attend to the trauma cases**
  An example would be someone with broken bones. They may be screaming in pain, but they will definitely live.

- **priority #3 — the walking wounded**
  These may be people with bruises, cuts, and scrapes, in various states of distress or shock — extremely sorry for themselves, but among the least of your present problems.

SHOCK

Shock sets in when the brain and other vital organs are deprived of oxygen due to inadequate blood circulation to the body tissues. Its development can be gradual or rapid. It is associated with a wide range of injuries, from severe bleeding and burns to spinal cord injuries and conditions affecting breathing, heart, and nerve functions. It is a killer, a steadily deteriorating condition that should be treated as early as possible.

Signs of shock include:

- **decreased consciousness**

- **shallow, irregular, difficult breathing**

- **a weak, rapid pulse**

- **pale, cold, clammy skin that turns increasingly bluish-grey**

- **bluish-purple colour to lips, tongue, earlobes, and fingernails (in dark-skinned people, the inside of the lips, the mouth, the tongue, and nail beds will be blue)**

- **profuse sweating**

- **vomiting**

- **anxiety, uneasiness, agitation**

- **confusion**

- **extreme thirst**

- **nausea**

- **faintness**

As the condition develops, the risk of systemic damage increases — that the condition may become irreversible and the patient will die.

You can only do your best, recalling as much as you can of whatever first aid training you may have received. You should make casualties as comfortable as possible. For a casualty with suspected head or spinal injuries, it would be best to leave them in the position found, creating support for their head and reassuringly telling them not to move, while hoping against hope that more qualified help will arrive. A person with a severely bleeding arm or leg should be placed on their back or in any more comfortable position, injuries permitting. In order to maintain an open airway, an unresponsive casualty should, ideally, be placed on his or her side in what is known as the recovery position.

In any case, body temperature must be maintained. A sleeping bag or blankets may not be enough to maintain adequate temperature for a victim in severe shock: you will need to supplement these measures with hot water bottles or other sources of heat including, perhaps, your own or someone else's body heat.

Keep victims as calm and reassured as possible. This is why blankets and warm cups of tea are traditional aspects of disaster response.

It is safe to say that most people involved in the shaking of a severe earthquake — including you — whether injured or not, will be in some degree of shock.

RESCUE AND RECOVERY

Following a megaquake, you and those around you may find yourselves faced with trapped and buried people. It may be possible for you to reach some of these; others you may be unable to reach. Some may be seriously injured, some may be dying, others may be dead. They could be strangers to you, or they might be friends or family.

The instincts of most able-bodied bystanders will be to carry out whatever rescue efforts they can. The official word on this is that inexperienced, ill-equipped members of the public should not put themselves at undue risk. In emergency situations, far too many untrained helpers get killed or injured by hazards that they did not anticipate — and create further hazards in the process. Trained, experienced, and professional help will be on the way, even if it seems like forever in coming.

WHAT TO DO WITH THE DEAD?

There will be bodies to deal with — perhaps many — not necessarily by you, but by somebody. It could be days before emergency services are in a position to remove the bodies. There is little in the way of official advice for the public on this semi-taboo subject. Until such time as clear instructions are widely published, you will have to let your own best judgement guide you.

The following are important words of advice gleaned from various official sources:

- **move bodies only if necessary**
  For example, move them off a street, into the shade, out of reach of animals, and away from places frequented by children. Move them only a short distance. One of the difficulties faced by the rescue services will be establishing the identities of victims — and one of the clues to a victim's identity may be knowing exactly where that person died. An exception to this guideline would be the recovery of a body by someone who knows the victim and is in a position to take charge of the victim's remains.

- **photograph bodies, if possible**
  — as a way of documenting the circumstances.

- **identify bodies, if possible**
  Label bodies with whatever information you can gather, even if it is only with a note stuffed into a pocket, such as "recovered from Joe's Deli — regular customer — first name may be Bob." Cover them, and report their presence to proper authorities as soon as the opportunity presents itself.

As one senior coroner put it to me, "If we can't get to the victims, you won't be able to get them to us. Place them in a cool spot, cover them, and get on with caring for yourself and the living."

BODY BAGS   These waterproof, odourproof, zippered nylon bags are designed to enclose and facilitate the transportation of human remains. Larger companies and organizations, including Block Watch committees, would be well advised to have some in stock; however, these bags will not be a feature of many personal emergency kits. That is why many of the victims of the Big One will be contained, initially, using the less dignified alternative of garbage bags and duct tape. *(For recommended suppliers of body bags, see Resources on our website, www.earthquakeprep.ca.)*

EMOTIONAL FIRST AID   The psychological impact of a major earthquake will be enormous for most of those caught up in it. Surroundings and most of the familiar things of life will lie almost unrecognizably crumpled. The world will have changed in an instant: thousands of people will have been catapulted into a new and bewildering reality. The disruption of daily life; being unable to sleep in their own bed, wake up, and do their daily routines; a narrow escape from death, perhaps, or someone else dying; being out of contact with family members and friends; being unable to go to work for weeks, or months, or ever: these and countless other factors will add up to huge stress for many people.

Likewise, the impact of the catastrophe on those coming to the rescue from outside the stricken area — professional responders and dedicated volunteers — will be immense. Everyone will be confronted by the dead and seriously injured, by shocked and distressed people, and by devastation everywhere.

Traumatized people will be in need of every kind of help. They will be in states of disbelief, confusion, disorientation, and anxiety. They will be experiencing numbness, anger, grief, despair, helplessness, and hopelessness. Their physical reactions will include trembling, diarrhea, nausea, increased heart rate, increase in blood pressure, difficulty in sleeping, and loss of appetite. For months afterwards, people will experience flashbacks — involuntary images of the event — and nightmares, panic attacks, and dull, enduring fear. There will be those mired in guilt at having survived, and others elated for exactly the same reason.

If you live in the southwestern corner of this province, you may be one of these people.

Children may be especially traumatized and will need all of the comforting, reassurance, acceptance, and loving attention they can get — and the establishing of whatever routines and security may be possible in a world fallen apart.

It is important to know that these responses and many more are to be expected — in others and oneself — and that it is absolutely okay to accept or seek help from whoever is in a position to offer it. In the first few days, these are likely to be untrained but compassionate, understanding, mentally and emotionally "available" neighbours and friends — people who have emerged relatively unscathed from the experience. In the days that follow, those providing help and reassurance will be semi-trained, caring volunteers and professional trauma counselors.

The world will be turned on end for those most closely caught up in this catastrophe. Things will not be "back to normal" for a very long time.

FIRST AID KITS

You should have an appropriate first aid kit — in a soft bag rather than a rigid case — in each of the following locations:

- **your home**

- **at least one of your home grab-and-go bags**

- **every workplace grab-and-go bag**

- **at least one grab-and-go bag in every vehicle**

That said, your first aid kit may be next to useless if you are not familiar with its contents and how to use them — quickly and efficiently, in a crisis situation, perhaps surrounded by victims in pain and onlookers who may be behaving hysterically or like zombies. There must be millions of ready made, "feel good" kits in the world whose owners have little idea what's inside.

If you take a first aid course, you will leave with an appropriate first aid instruction booklet — one that will probably only be useful to you if you use it to keep alive your memory of what you learned in the course.

Ideally, assemble your own kits, using the following suggestions as a starting point.

ESSENTIAL EQUIPMENT

For any instruments, go for quality: you will want instruments that work well.

- **digital thermometer**
  Easy to use. Probe covers available. Sterilize with any suitable disinfectant.

- **universal or super scissors**
  Cut through almost anything, including heavy clothing and vehicle seat belts.

- **bandage scissors (5 1/2" — with blunt and sharp points)**
  Stainless steel scissors for cutting tape, dressings, light clothing, etc.

- **splinter forceps/tweezers**
  For removal of splinters and foreign objects from the skin.

- **small magnifying glass**
  For spotting slivers, especially glass splinters.

- **penlight**
  Use to locate splinters or objects in eyes, ears, or throat — or if light is poor. If with internal battery, note expiry date. Otherwise store fresh batteries separately.

- **needles**
  For removing splinters. Keep in small bag with tweezers and antiseptic wipes *(see below)*.

- **instant ice packs**
  For burns, sprains, and nosebleeds. Squeeze to activate. Note the expiry date. If you have access to ice, use it in a plastic bag — it will last much longer than an instant pack.

- **CPR mask and airways (assorted sizes, 50 mm - 110 mm)**
  For airway management, including choking. For use by those with CPR training.

WOUND MANAGEMENT ITEMS

- **irrigation syringe (20/30/60 cc/ml)**
  For flushing dirt and debris from wounds. Use cleanest possible water.

- **butterfly closure strips or steri strips**
  Invaluable wound closures — an alternative to sutures (stitches).

- **Benzalkonium chloride antiseptic wipes**
  for cleaning around wounds (not wound itself); sterilizing a thermometer probe, needle, or tweezer ends; and cleaning hands.

- **baby wipes**
  (in sealed packages)
  For cleaning around wounds and general cleaning up.

- **bottled wound cleanser**
  For washing wounds. Avoid hydrogen peroxide.

- **non-sterile gauze pads (4" x 4")**
  For wound cleaning with a wound cleanser; or as a soaker/pressure dressing placed over a sterile wound dressing and under a roll bandage.

- **examination gloves**
  Wear when administering first aid to other persons to avoid contact with body fluids. Note: latex gloves can cause allergic reactions.

- **infection control bags**
  Orange plastic bags for the disposal of contaminated materials.

- **sterile gauze dressings (4" x 4")**
  For dressing cuts and scrapes, wound cleansing, and skin preparation before bandaging.

- **Telfa or similar non-adherent sterile dressings (3" x 4" or larger)**
  The first item to apply to a wound. You can always cut larger pads down.

- **abdominal (ABD) pads (8" x 10")**
  For large wounds — very absorbent.

- **gauze roll bandages (3" or 4")**
  To secure dressings to wounds.

- **tensor (crepe) bandages (3" or 4")**
  For compression of dressings, or to secure splints or hot or cold packs.

- **adhesive tape (1" and 2")**
  To secure dressings. Does not adhere well to wet or sweaty skin.

- **self-adhesive tape (2")**
  The equivalent of gauze, tensor bandage, and adhesive tape combined — a very efficient, self-adhesive bandage.

- **compress dressings (4" x 6" and larger)**
  Non-stick, absorbent pad with gauze roll or tensor (crepe) bandage attached (much like a World War II field dressing). For control of major bleeding, hard-to-bandage areas, and bandaging oneself. An excellent "quick fix."

- **burn dressings (12" x 12", 18" x 18", and 36" x 36")**
  Sterile dressings to be applied immediately to minor burns.

- **assorted small wound bandages**
  Including finger tip and knuckle dressings.

- **safety pins**
  Assorted sizes

- **cotton-tipped applicators (such as Q-Tips)**
  For removing something from eye, cleansing small wounds, etc.

- **triangular bandages (approx. 40" x 40" x 56")**
  Lots of them. Use for splints, or as a sling, or to form an extra-broad bandage. Consider making your own from old sheets.

- **eye pads (minimum of two)**
  Provide comfort and protection for eye injuries. Both eyes should be covered; otherwise, an injured eye will follow movements of the exposed eye.

- **eye bath, saline (sterile salt water) for irridation**
  Early care for eye injuries.

- **Esmarch rubber bandage**
  For use as tourniquet — to be used only by those with suitable training.

MEDICATIONS

- **Extra Strength Tylenol and Kids' Tylenol**
  For pain, headache, or fever control.

- **sugar/glucose gel**
  To treat diabetes insulin shock.

- **any essential medications**
  (See also Section 10, Toiletries and Medications.)

MISCELLANEOUS ITEMS

- **Sam splint**
  To splint possible fractures, including neck injuries.

- **tongue depressors**
  For examining a casualty's mouth and throat. Can also be used as finger splints.

- **sunscreen (SPF30-plus for maximum protection)**
  High-quality, waterproof, and fragrance-free.

- **whistle**
  For attracting attention. The sound of a good whistle carries further than yelling and can be sustained long after the voice has given out. *(See also Section 22, Communications.)*

- **foil blankets (several)**
  Early care for hypothermia. Wrap around injured person to avoid loss of body heat (important tip: cover the head, leaving space for breathing). Useful as a rain shield. *(See also Section 8, Heat/Warmth.)*

- **wool blanket**
  Early care for hypothermia. Wool retains measure of warmth even when wet. Comforting in almost any situation.

- **notebook and pen**
  For making any important notes (patient assessment record).

- **largest size ziplock bags**
  Divide the contents of your kit into these bags, which will then be available for any other needs.

The Workers' Compensation Board's *WorkSafe* Occupational, Health & Safety Regulations and the Canadian Labour Code lay down levels of first aid kits and training for every kind and category of business and organization. If you are responsible for a business or organization that does not yet meet these requirements, please be in touch with your local authority.

FIRST AID CHECKLIST

FIRST AID KITS

You have an appropriate size kit:

    at home ☐

    in at least one home grab-and-go bag ☐

    in each workplace grab-and-go bag ☐

    in at least one vehicle grab-and-go bag in every vehicle that your household owns ☐

FIRST AID TRAINING

The following family members have completed:

    a current first aid course

        Name: _____ **Date:** _____

        Name: _____ **Date:** _____

        Name: _____ **Date:** _____

    a current artificial respiration course

        Name: _____ **Date:** _____

        Name: _____ **Date:** _____

        Name: _____ **Date:** _____

The following family members are thoroughly familiar with the contents of your first aid kits and know how to use them

    Name: _____

    Name: _____

    Name: _____

DISASTER RESPONSE ROUTES

You may have seen the disaster response route signs (a black-and-yellow triangle within a black-and-yellow circle) that are being posted on strategic routes in southwestern BC. These routes will be among the first to be cleared of obstructions and debris following a major earthquake. They are designed to be the lifelines used by fire, police, ambulance and other emergency services in their efforts to get help and supplies to wherever they are most needed — possibly to you. The government and emergency services are counting on the public's co-operation in keeping clear of these routes following any major disaster. *(For further information, visit the Ministry of Transportation and Highways website, www.th.gov.bc.ca, and click on Disaster Response Routes.)*

Hypothermia, sometimes called exposure, occurs when the body loses heat faster than it can produce it. It can occur rapidly, even at relatively warm temperatures, as the body temperature drops due to prolonged exposure to cold, wet, or windy conditions. It will occur even more rapidly when the body temperature drops as a result of immersion in cold water or exposure to the elements. And it can be fatal.

You need to be able to recognize the signs and know how to help someone with hypothermia. You also need to know how to avoid hypothermia yourself.

EARLY SIGNS

Symptoms will vary with each individual. It usually begins with fatigue and weakness. Muscles become tense, but shivering can be overcome by activity. Treatment: get the person out of the cold, wind, rain, or water. Do whatever you can to warm them up. See beyond protestations of "I'm fine!" Then check for signs of hypothermia in yourself and other members of your party. Don't be shy: what you are confronting is the beginning of something that, improperly handled, can kill.

MILD HYPOTHERMIA

Uncontrolled, intense shivering. The victim is still alert, but movements are becoming less co-ordinated. Treatment: get the victim out of wet clothes and into dry ones if you possibly can. Cover him or her with blankets or get them into a sleeping bag. Prevent further heat loss, Allow the body to re-warm itself.

> In adverse conditions, 80 per cent of body heat is lost through the head. When wrapping up — or wrapping someone else up — keep the head warm!

MODERATE TO SEVERE HYPOTHERMIA

Shivering slows and eventually stops. Muscles stiffen and the victim becomes very clumsy and unco-ordinated. Exhaustion, mental confusion, memory lapses, and apathy set in. Speech becomes increasingly slurred and breathing becomes slower and shallower. The victim is gradually losing consciousness. Treatment: ideally, get the victim into a pre-warmed sleeping bag with another person — even better, sandwiched between two people. Skin-to-skin contact, especially around the chest and neck, is most effective. Handle the victim gently, avoiding jolts that might disrupt the heart's functioning. Warm the victim as best you can to stabilize temperature only: too rapid a rise in temperature may prove fatal. Ignore pleas of "I'm okay, leave me alone." If the victim is fully conscious and able to swallow, offer sips of warm, sweet, non-alcoholic liquids. Be prepared to stay put until the victim is out of danger.

CRITICAL HYPOTHERMIA

The victim is unconscious. The skin is cold, the body rigid. There are no apparent signs of breathing and the pulse is faint. Treatment: handle the victim with great care to avoid cardiac arrest. Start rescue breathing, keeping a close watch for vital sign changes. Do not administer CPR, because CPR can kill a hypothermia victim — and in any case, this emergency measure will prove useless if CPR is not followed promptly by shock provided by a trained user of an automatic external defibrillator (or similar device).

Don't allow yourself or anyone in your party to get anywhere near this critical point. Getting unduly cold and/or wet can have devastating consequences. Act early.

PRECAUTIONS

These all have to do with awareness and common sense:

- Be prepared for adverse conditions. Wrap up, cover up. Keep dry and out of the wind: rain can be a killer. Use layering. Bear in mind that wool retains a measure of warmth even when wet.

- Know the signs of hypothermia and appropriate responses.

- Have immediate access to spare, dry clothing (including a toque) and, ideally, a sleeping bag and a space blanket, survival bag, or Extreme Survivor suit *(see Section 8, Heat and Warmth).*

> CAUTION: Although the above advice is drawn from reliable sources, the author is not a medical doctor and you would be wise to learn more about this subject. *(See also Section 16, First Aid.)*

HYPOTHERMIA REVIEW

SIGNS

**Everyone in your household is familiar
with the different stages of hypothermia** ☐

TREATMENT

**Everyone in your household is familiar
with the correct ways to respond to hypothermia** ☐

PRECAUTIONS

**Everyone in your household is familiar
with the precautions against hypothermia** ☐

The following excerpts are from *The Province's* two-day special of July 23-24, 2000 entitled "The Big One":

continued from page 152

GREATER VICTORIA

Severe shaking and underwater slides damage almost two-thirds of the harbour, affecting docks, piers and cranes. There is general panic and considerable damage, even to buildings especially built to withstand earthquakes. Buildings are knocked off kilter and shift off foundations. Some buildings collapse completely, others partially. There are numerous cracks in the ground. Some underground pipes are broken, leading in places to fires. The shaking plays havoc with the Sooke Reservoir containment dam....

Some high-rise apartments collapse with the loss of hundreds of lives. The Royal Jubilee Hospital suffers extensive damage, knocking it out of action. The Victoria General Hospital suffers significant damage. The recently built Island Highway suffers damage in numerous areas, but is still usable. Only emergency vehicles will be allowed to use it....

Gas, water and power lines are cracked, leaving more than 60 per cent of the area without power and water. The leaking Sooke dam plays havoc with firefighting.

Victoria International Airport is closed. The control tower has collapsed, there is major structural damage to the terminal and liquefaction of the soil has cracked and heaved the runways.

EXPECTED VANCOUVER ISLAND CASUALTIES:

Fatalities	1,000
Requiring hospitalization	5,000
Requiring medical attention	40,000

EXPECTED VANCOUVER ISLAND BUILDING DAMAGE:

Percentage of structures uninhabitable due to heavy damage:

Single-family homes — wood-frame	30%
Single-family homes — unreinforced masonry	50%
Low-rise	30%
Medium-rise*	30%
High-rise (most types)	20%
Schools — built before 1940	60%
Schools — newer or improved	20%

* A further 60% of medium-rise buildings could sustain moderate damage but remain habitable.[22]

continued on page 210

T HERE WILL BE OUT-OF-CONTROL FIRES OF every type and size raging in many parts of southwestern British Columbia and the United States Pacific Northwest. Fire departments will be fighting blaze after blaze with whatever equipment has survived the quake — equipment designed for normal times. With more simultaneous fires than this region has ever seen, firefighters will be faced with a number of colossal problems:

- **lack of access** — downed bridges, crumpled overpasses, and highways and streets blocked by debris and abandoned vehicles will hamper and block their every move.

- **ruptured water lines** which, in many cases, will make a nightmarishly difficult job impossible.

- **injured and dying people in unprecedented numbers** — people who, in normal times, would be receiving the undivided attention of firefighters or paramedics.

This chaotic situation will be made worse as every firefighter, just like every other emergency services worker still at his or her post, will be taking care of the greater need while knowing that their own home situation and loved ones are in disarray and vulnerable.

FIRE EXTINGUISHERS

These could save your home, your livelihood, or your life — at any time, let alone in the aftermath of a megaquake. Plenty of people will lose everything in the Big One for lack of adequate firefighting equipment but, with preparation and good luck, you need not be among them.

Extinguishers should be dry chemical, multipurpose, ABC rated (covering oil, gasoline, flammable liquid, electrical, trash, wood, paper and cloth fires), with a pressurized cargo of at least 2.27 kg (5 lbs) and a pressure gauge. For your kitchen, however, you might choose a BC rated extinguisher because of the easier clean-up of its contents (ABC powder will fuse to hot surfaces).

Extinguishers should be attached firmly by their brackets to walls or other suitable fixing points. Unsecured, they may become lost in the general debris. Keep them close to an exit, with the kitchen extinguisher well away from the stove.

You should have:

- **a suitable extinguisher for each floor of your home**
  Don't forget your garage, workshop, and basement.

- **a suitable extinguisher for each vehicle**

- **suitable extinguishers in your workplace**

Everyone in your household and workplace should know:

- **the location of your extinguishers**

- **how to use them — instinctively**

Before using an extinguisher, get everyone out of the immediate area and call (or have someone else call) 911.

TECHNIQUE To use a fire extinguisher:

1. **Pull the pin on the extinguisher.**

2. **Aim at the base of the fire (standing about two metres/six feet away from the fire).**

3. **Squeeze the handle of the extinguisher.**

4. **Sweep the extinguisher from side to side while aiming at the base of the fire.**

> IMPORTANT: An extinguisher that has been used, even briefly, should be considered empty and be refilled as soon as possible.

Could you and everyone in your household find the extinguishers in your home and use them effectively — in the dark, or with eyes partially closed by smoke, or just in the shocked, dazed state in which you may find yourselves immediately following a major earthquake? That is exactly how you might be required to use them.

The decision to fight a fire yourself is critical. If you feel you can snuff out a blaze with a fire extinguisher, do so quickly, but don't linger if the fire starts to get out of hand. Get out of the house, doing your best to ensure that everyone else does the same. Once outside, stay out.

> IMPORTANT: If you regularly use a wood-burning fireplace or stove, have the chimney or flue cleaned at least once a year. And keep a container of water nearby. Water doused on a fire creates instant steam and the rising steam will extinguish a fire in the chimney or flue — out of reach of the contents of a fire extinguisher.

You should have at least one smoke detector on every floor of your home — possibly combined with the carbon monoxide detectors that you should have if there are any combustion appliances in your home (for example, a gas stove, fridge, or furnace; a wood-burning fireplace or stove; or a fuel-burning portable appliance — *see Section 19, Carbon Monoxide Poisoning*). Test your detectors monthly using smoke from a blown-out candle. Replace detectors every 10 years. Use only top-quality, non-rechargeable batteries, and replace these every six months *(see Section 27, Check-ups)*.

Smoke kills. The gases emitted by a fire are deadly. Most fire fatalities happen during the night when people are sleeping. The gases lull victims into an even deeper sleep from which they never awake. In these and many other instances, the only thing standing between a safe escape and deadly fumes is a properly functioning smoke alarm.

A fire can cause the temperature to rise several hundred degrees in a matter of seconds. It can render you unconscious, cutting off any opportunity to escape. Heat that intense can cause the human body to stop functioning altogether.

A residential home can be totally consumed by fire in less than five minutes. You therefore need a warning — smoke alarms throughout the home — and an escape plan to get out in time.

Read and follow the detailed instructions for location and installation that will accompany any reputable smoke alarm.

SMOKE (AND CARBON MONOXIDE) DETECTORS

These specially designed ladders can save lives when other escape routes are impossible. Ideally, you will have one for every upper floor of your home that has no alternative means of escape (i.e., an exit other than the main stairs).

The ideal model will probably be made of plastic with aluminum rungs. It will attach easily and quickly to any window sill, with the unopened ladder hanging on the outside of the window. When released, the ladder will fall, tangle-free, and provide a stable, relatively easy means of descent. Two-storey models are readily available, and three-storey versions can be obtained as special orders. *(For recommended manufacturers and retailers, see Resources on our website, www.earthquakeprep.ca.)*

Everyone in your household will need to practise mounting your ladder in a window in a ready position for deployment. It is vital that you be completely familiar with the operation of these ladders prior to needing one in an emergency.

Flexible rope ladders are available. Their disadvantages are that they may tangle and will almost certainly be less easy to descend than a more rigid ladder. And a suitable rope, while providing an effective means of escape for anyone with adequate physical ability and experience, could prove disastrous for anyone with inadequate strength and dexterity.

EMERGENCY ESCAPE LADDERS

**EMERGENCY ESCAPE
SMOKE HOODS**

Three out of four fire fatalities are caused by smoke inhalation. The most important element in surviving a fire can be maintaining a source of breathable air. Your survival could depend on your having an emergency escape smoke hood with you when you need it.

These devices consist of a filter the size of a soft-drink can attached to a transparent, flexible hood that completely covers the head and neck. The chemical catalytic filter provides up to 15 minutes of protection from toxic carbon monoxide and other gases, the number one killer in fires. The hood protects the head and eyes from smoke — black, choking smoke that can immobilize you in just a few seconds — and from transient flames, without interfering with visibility or hearing. One size fits all, unaffected by eyeglasses, hair length, or facial hair (although they are unsuitable for children under the age of about 10). With a shelf life of 5 years, they are designed for one-time use only.

If you live, work, or do business in a high-rise, travel and stay in hotels, are elderly or disabled, use a wheelchair — or for any reason could find yourself in any situation where immediate escape is difficult

---

BE PREPARED! At about 11:00 p.m. one April night in 1974, while I was a guest in my mother's house in London, England, I was getting ready for bed when I heard a thud in the living room below — the sound, as it turned out, of a paraffin stove being knocked over by my six-month old puppy. I reached the living room within three or four seconds to find the room engulfed in flames and oily smoke.

I then did two things that, with hindsight and subsequent training, I wouldn't dream of doing now. I aimed a large, water-filled fire extinguisher into the blaze, not realizing how ineffectual water would be on an oil-based fire. That wasted several seconds. And I opened the front door long enough to bellow into the darkness, "Fire! Dial 999! Fire! Dial 999!" as I booted Scrubber, my beared collie, the mother of my puppy, into the street. That wasted another few seconds — and let in a blast of fire-fuelling oxygen.

I had already yelled to my mother, asleep upstairs, to alert her, and as I started up the stairs I took in my first full inhalation of smoke. It stopped me in my tracks: in an instant, it shut down my breathing. I knew that a second such inhalation would be my last.

My military macau, in his large, stainless steel cage in the living room, was vapourized in the inferno, along with much else. My puppy I found the next morning in the back yard, cold and stiff, wrapped in a water-soaked blanket by one of the firemen who had arrived very soon after I sounded the alarm. Scrubber turned up the next day after a night in the open, bewildered but unharmed. And my mother probably knew very little of what happened. I had shouted up to her from the garden below her second floor window, urging her to come to the window, but received no reply. She died of asphyxiation, as do so many victims in fires.

I was well trained as a light infantry officer: I knew exactly what to do under fire, but not in a fire. I was well educated, reasonably intelligent, and capable, but I made fundamental mistakes that night. One of them was to try to save the house. In the moment, my lack of training and experience told.

No smoke alarms... an unsecured paraffin heater.... Now, as I look at one of the emergency escape smoke hoods described above, I wish that they had been invented then. If my mother had had one beside her bed, she would almost certainly have survived.

or impossible — one of these hoods could be your only means of survival. Expensive at just over $100 Cdn? Not really, if it saves your life. And, if one of the hoods that we recommend is used in a fire emergency, you will get a full refund from the manufacturer.

Remember: circumstances can change from normal to deadly in moments, just when you least expect it. *(For emergency escape smoke hood retailers, see Resources on our website, www.earthquakeprep.ca.)*

EMERGENCY ROLL-CALL AND CONTACT LISTS

If you live in a building with more than three or four units or suites, there should be a typed list of the names, suite numbers, and telephone numbers of everyone living in the building, along with emergency contact names and telephone numbers for those people. This list should be kept in a protective plastic folder in a secure but easily accessible place, either near the main entrance or wherever everyone will assemble outside if the building is evacuated.

There is a privacy issue here, but it is worth addressing: lives and much else may be at stake.

Every company or organization with employees should likewise have an emergency roll-call and contact list *(see also Section 22, Communications).*

PLANNING

Plan with your family. What you will be discussing really might happen. Drum into everyone's head how terrifyingly quickly a fire can take start and spread — taking you completely by surprise. One moment you are cooking normally; the next, the stove top and hood are ablaze. Be aware of the potential fire hazards in your home — the obvious ones (stove tops, fireplaces, candles, smoking, etc.) and the not-so-obvious ones (faulty and overloaded wiring, for example).

Plan two escape routes out of every room, especially bedrooms. If you live in a multi-storey apartment building, be familiar with the routes to exit stairways on your floor and other floors of the building. If your building has one or more elevators, plan to use the stairway, never the elevator. Elevators may become trapped between floors or take you directly to the fire.

Sleep with your bedroom doors closed at night. A closed door will help slow the spread of deadly fire, smoke, and heat. When following your escape route, close doors behind you to reduce the amount of oxygen reaching the fire.

Your smoke alarm may be your first warning of a fire — or the sound of a whistle or shouting from a family member. Respond instantly. If a closed door separates you from a possible fire, touch the door. If it feels cool, open it a crack to check for smoke. Be prepared to crawl on your hands and knees, below the worst of the smoke. If the door feels hot when you touch it, do not open it — use an alternative means of escape.

Disabled people have special needs and should have two escape plans — one for when the rest of the family is at home, and one for when alone. For more home fire escape tips for the disabled, contact your local fire department.

SHELTER

If you can't leave your room or apartment, create a shelter for yourself by sealing cracks around doors and vents, using wet towels, clothing, or bed linen if possible. This may be your only means of surviving a fire in a high-rise.

Open a window. If you can, telephone the fire department to tell them exactly where you are in the building. Shout for help, using a bright cloth item to signal your position. Use your whistle.

> TIP: If your clothes catch fire, stop in your tracks, drop to the ground, and roll over and over to put out the flames. Do not run. Running will only increase the flames.

MEETING PLACE

Gather at a pre-determined meeting place outside your home, well away from the building, and take a head count. Once outside, stay out. Send someone to a neighbour's house to telephone the fire department. Meet the fire trucks and tell firefighters whether everyone is out of the house.

PRACTISE

If you practise your fire drills on a regular basis, you and others will act swiftly and accurately when an emergency happens. Rehearse every three months, with snap alarms called at random times. If you don't practise — in other words, if you don't take this seriously — you are unlikely to do the right things in a crisis. Mistakes can cost lives.

FIREPROOF CONTAINERS

Keep all of your valuable documents and records — birth certificates, marriage certificates, passports, social insurance cards, immunization records, wills, contracts, deeds, banking and investment files, insurance policies, photographs, important telephone numbers, photocopies of your vehicle papers, etc. — in one or more secure and fireproof places. Why? So that you won't lose them in a disaster. The tragedy is that, in the Big One, so many people will lose their important documents. At home, you could use a fireproof filing cabinet or one or more portable fireproof boxes (*available from office equipment stores*). There is a limit, after all, to what you can squash into a bank safety deposit box (and banks will probably be closed in the immediate aftermath of a megaquake).

ACKNOWLEDGEMENT: The information above is drawn in part from First Alert literature. You may wish to visit their website, *www.firstalert.com*, or contact them at 1-800 722-1938.

FIRE CHECKLIST

This checklist is for fire precautions for your home, vehicle, and workplace. Remember: you may not need all of the options listed below. Just check and implement the ones that feel right for you.

FIRE EXTINGUISHERS

You have a:

suitable fire extinguisher for each floor of your home ☐

suitable fire extinguisher for each vehicle ☐

workplace well equipped with fire extinguishers ☐

Everyone in your household knows:

the location of your fire extinguishers — even in the dark ☐

how to use extinguishers effectively — literally with their eyes shut ☐

SMOKE AND CARBON MONOXIDE DETECTORS

You have a:

suitable smoke and carbon monoxide detector for each floor of your home ☐

workplace well equipped with smoke detectors ☐

EMERGENCY ESCAPE LADDERS

If applicable, you have:

an escape ladder for each floor of your home ☐

a suitable escape rope for each floor of your home ☐

Caution: a rope is a poor substitute for a ladder because many people are insufficiently experienced or fit to descend a rope safely.

EMERGENCY ROLL-CALL OR CONTACT LIST

If applicable, you have an:

up-to-date list of tenants and/or owners in your multi-unit building ☐

up-to-date list of employees in your workplace ☐

FIREPROOF CONTAINERS

You have a fireproof filing cabinet, fireproof safe, or fireproof box ☐

FIRE REVIEW

You have a carefully thought-out evacuation plan for your household ☐

Everyone in the household is familiar with the points in this section — and how serious a fire can be ☐

You will be practising your fire drills often enough to ensure that they become second nature ☐

How quickly any business or organization recovers from a major earthquake will depend to a large extent on how well its people emerge from their own ordeals. Employees whose home lives are in tatters as a result of the earthquake will likely be slower returning to work than those who were well prepared.

C ARBON MONOXIDE (CO) IS AN INVISIBLE, colourless, odourless gas — and it's deadly. Because you can't see, taste, or smell it, it can kill you or your family without you even knowing it's there. It suffocates the victim from the inside out.

> Many deaths during the January 1998 Quebec Ice Storm resulted from fire, hypothermia, and carbon monoxide poisoning.
> Alex Tilley, founder and owner of Tilley Endurables Inc.

THE SILENT KILLER

Carbon monoxide is produced by the incomplete combustion of natural gas, propane, fuel oil, gasoline, kerosene, paraffin, coal, charcoal, or wood — the fuels that we use for our furnaces, barbecues, grills, clothes dryers, ranges, ovens, fireplaces, water heaters, space heaters, wood-burning stoves, and automobiles. Vents and chimneys usually remove the products of combustion from a building, but if a vent is not effective or a chimney is clogged, the products of combustion will spill into the home. Leaving a car running in an attached garage, barbecuing indoors, faulty or improperly installed appliances, and poor ventilation can all cause carbon monoxide levels to rise rapidly.

Carbon monoxide is absorbed through the lungs into the bloodstream. In its early stages, it produces flu-like symptoms such as headaches, drowsiness, nausea, dizziness, impaired judgement, irritability, and loss of co-ordination. High concentrations can lead to unconsciousness, brain damage, and death. Especially at risk are the unborn, infants, children, pregnant women, the elderly, smokers, and people with respiratory health concerns, lung or heart disease, or a weakened immune system.

Because many illnesses cause similar symptoms, carbon monoxide poisoning is difficult to diagnose. All too often a patient with flu-like symptoms has been sent home by a doctor to rest — back to the environment that caused the symptoms — and has subsequently become permanently disabled, or died. Unlike the flu, carbon monoxide poisoning does not cause a rise in body temperature.

CHECKING FOR CO POISONING

If you ever wonder whether you may be suffering from the slow effects carbon monoxide poisoning, here are some checks:

- Do you have or use anything in your home that creates combustion — for example, a gas stove, fireplace, water heater; a wood-burning fireplace; or a portable heater or stove that uses fuel? Do you warm up an automobile in your garage or another enclosed space? If the answers to these questions is "No," your symptoms are unlikely to be a result of carbon monoxide poisoning. If you do have anything in your home that creates combustion:

  - Find out whether other members of your household are feeling sick as well.
  - See whether you feel better when you leave home for a period of time.

To be absolutely sure, see a physician and request a carboxyhemoglobin test. This will determine the percentage of carbon monoxide in your blood.

> IMPORTANT: If you find yourself suffering from any of the symptoms above and carbon monoxide could possibly be the cause, don't lie down and rest. Call your fire department and get out into the fresh air.

HOW TO AVOID IT
Never completely seal a room from drafts. All burning appliances consume oxygen and, for complete combustion, there must be adequate ventilation and proper venting to the outdoors. This is why energy conservation — substantial caulking, draftproofing, and insulation — can be a double-edged sword. It may save energy and money, but it can also result in there being inadequate air for appliance and vent operation.

BC Gas warns that when undertaking substantial draftproofing, or when adding a high-volume kitchen or bathroom exhaust fan, a licenced gas or ventilation contractor be brought in to determine whether additional air supply is necessary. All appliances and vents should be properly installed and regularly inspected and serviced — and manufacturers' operating instructions followed.

Never operate barbecue grills indoors and never leave an automobile running in a closed garage.

> RECENT research indicates that low levels of exposure to carbon monoxide over time may cause neurological damage which may not be repairable.

CARBON MONOXIDE ALARMS
For safety's sake, get as many alarms as you need. Quality and additional features are important. The alarms you buy should be battery powered or have battery back-up, because your greatest need is likely to be when the power is off and you're managing with

emergency means of heating, lighting, and cooking. (Please note: the battery back-up feature of 110 volt models may only operate for a few hours after the power fails.)

A carbon monoxide alarm is not a substitute for a smoke alarm. If you don't already have adequate smoke detectors, consider investing in one or more combined carbon monoxide/smoke alarms.

Look for these features:

- **UL, ULC, CUL, IAS or CSA listed**
  Look for "Certified to CSA standard CAN/CGA-6.19" and the CSA blue flame logo.

- **favourable rating**
  Consumer Reports offers independent evaluations.

- **as long a warranty as possible**

- **electro-chemical sensor or tin oxide technology**

- **digital display of carbon monoxide (CO) concentration in parts-per-million**
  The digital display reading on an installed alarm should read "zero." There should be no carbon monoxide in your home.

- **peak-level display**
  This shows the highest reading since you last cleared the unit. If you press the button, you should see "zero." If you see a reading higher than zero, you will know that a carbon monoxide incident has occurred — and you should do some serious investigation into how it occurred. If the reason isn't readily apparent, immediately get professional help in tracing it.

> IMPORTANT: Regardless of the model chosen, it is vital that you respond to any and all audible alarms — none should be ignored.

There are only two ways to know whether you have carbon monoxide in your home. One is to get sick and possibly die. The other is to have a carbon monoxide alarm. There's no other way to tell.

LOCATION

You should have a carbon monoxide alarm on every level of your home, but especially near living and sleeping areas. These are the locations where people are most vulnerable.

At 400 parts-per-million, death can occur after three hours at that level of exposure. If this happens while a person is asleep — maybe in bed, maybe on the sofa — and they are not alerted by an alarm, chances are they will die in their sleep.

Because carbon monoxide gas mixes rapidly with air, a carbon monoxide alarm can be installed anywhere in a room or corridor and provide effective warning.

TRUST YOUR ALARM If a smoke alarm sounds, all of your senses will come into play in determining whether there is a problem or if the alarm is merely malfunctioning. Smoke, after all, is pretty obvious. But when a carbon monoxide alarm goes off, it's different: carbon monoxide is invisible, odourless, and tasteless, so none of your senses can detect it. That's why people have an often tragic habit of not believing their carbon monoxide alarms. A visual reading above zero will help to convince you that there truly has been a carbon monoxide incident, not a false alarm.

Read and diligently follow the user's guide that comes with every alarm.

> ACKNOWLEDGEMENT: The above information is drawn in part from First Alert and Kidde plc sources and materials. You may wish to visit their websites, *www.firstalert.com* and *www.kiddesafety.com* or contact them at 1-800 722-1938 and 1-800 880-6788 respectively. And to complete the picture you should contact BC Gas (see your *SuperPages* or visit the BC Gas website, *www.bcgas.com*) for their excellent carbon monoxide information.

CARBON MONOXIDE POISONING CHECKLIST

CARBON MONOXIDE DETECTORS

You have an appropriate number installed in your home ☐
(battery operated or with battery back-up)

CARBON MONOXIDE/SMOKE DETECTORS

You have an appropriate number installed in your home ☐
(battery operated or with battery back-up)

REVIEW

PREVENTION

Everyone in your household is familiar with how to avoid ☐
carbon monoxide poisoning

More than half of BC households use natural gas as their primary energy source. It is a safe and reliable source, but you should understand its characteristics:

- Natural gas is odourless, so an odourant smelling like sulphur or rotten eggs is added to make it easy to detect small leaks.

- Natural gas is lighter than air. If leaked outdoors, it tends to rise and dissipate into the atmosphere.

- If leaked in a confined space, such as inside your home, natural gas mixes with air and forms a combustible mixture which can be ignited by sparks from electrical switches or appliances, or from open flames such as matches and pilot lights. Given the right mixture, a fire or explosion could result.

> WARNING: Every time you operate an electrical switch, plug, or appliance, or use a regular flashlight or lantern, a spark occurs inside the fitting or unit. That spark could be enough to ignite a build-up of gas, as would any open flame.

If you are in a building supplied with natural gas when a major earthquake happens, or if immediately afterwards you enter a building supplied with natural gas, these are procedures you should follow:

- **extinguish cigarettes, open flames, and fires**

- **don't light a match or smoke**

- **don't operate any light or other electrical switch — leave them as found**

- **don't plug in or unplug any electrical cord or appliance**

- **don't use a regular flashlight or battery-operated lantern**

- **don't create any other source of ignition — until you are confident that there is no escaping gas or, if gas is escaping, until the problem is rectified**

AVOIDING AN EXPLOSION

DETECTING ESCAPING GAS

- **inspect the gas appliances, pipes, and vents**
  If you need a light source, use an intrinsically safe (non-sparking) flashlight or a lightstick *(see Section 7, Lighting)*.

- **listen and smell for escaping gas**
  The most obvious signs to check for will be a hissing sound and/or a rotten egg smell.

IF LEAK IS DETECTED

- **leave the premises immediately — ventilating the building by opening doors and windows as you leave**

- **shut off the main gas supply at the meter**
  (See below for directions.)

- **evacuate everyone to at least 100 metres (325 feet) from the building**

Normally, you would then call the BC Gas 24-hour emergency line, 1-800 663-9911. Following a major earthquake, however, your telephone is unlikely to be working *(see Section 22, Communications)*.

TURNING OFF A GAS SUPPLY

This is easy. You will need a 30 cm to 40 cm (12" to 16") adjustable wrench or a special gas shut-off tool. Locate the shut-off valve. However complex the gas meter assembly, the valve will be just above the point where the gas line comes out of the ground. When the supply is "on," the shut-off valve is in line with the pipe, allowing the gas to flow through. To shut the flow of gas, turn the valve a quarter turn in either direction so that it is across the line of the pipe.

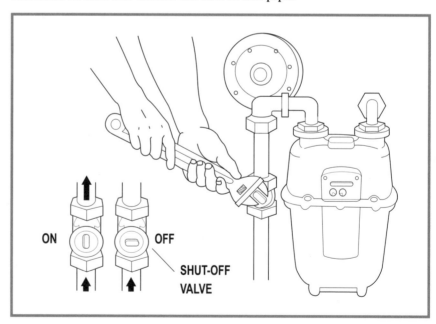

You should also turn off a gas supply if:

- **a gas appliance or water tank has broken loose from its connections**

- **a building has been seriously damaged**

- **there is, or has been, a fire**
  In the event of a fire, turn off the gas after you have evacuated the premises — if doing so does not endanger your life

Keep a suitable crescent or pipe wrench (oiled and thoroughly protected in plastic to prevent corrosion) or a shut-off tool close to your gas meter, ready for use. Keep it in a place known to everyone in your household but not where some helpful but ill-informed person may be tempted to use it without your permission.

If there are no discernible gas leaks but the vent of a particular appliance (i.e., your furnace, water heater, or fireplace) is broken or disconnected:

DAMAGED VENTS

- **turn off the gas supply to that particular appliance**
  Each appliance is equipped with its own shut-off valve. In the off position, the handle of the shut-off valve is at a right angle to the pipe *(see illustration)*.

- **do not operate a gas appliance with a broken or damaged vent**
  Dangerous levels of carbon monoxide can result.

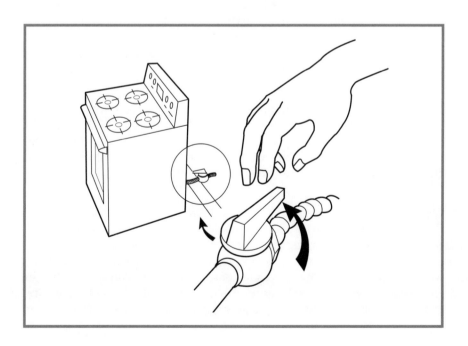

DO NOT turn off a gas supply unless there is a good reason for doing so. When a gas supply is turned off, pilot lights are extinguished. Before the gas is turned back on, the pipes must be pressure tested and the vents and appliances thoroughly inspected — normally, by a licenced gas fitter. While you are waiting for the supply to be reinstated by a qualified fitter, you will be without energy from this particular source (which is why you should have alternative means of cooking and heating — *see Section 6, Cooking and Section 8, Heat and Warmth*).

AUTOMATIC SHUT-OFF SYSTEMS

An earthquake-actuated gas shut-off valve may or may not be the right option for you. It will safeguard your home and provide peace of mind by automatically turning off the gas supply in a large earthquake — whether there's anyone home or not. It will do so immediately, and because it shuts off the supply at the meter outside, it protects the building from any leaks inside caused by the shaking of the earthquake.

These mechanical shut-off valves have been available for over 25 years. They are currently installed on nearly every school, hospital, college, university, and government building in the western half of BC as well as many commercial, industrial, and residential properties. The right model can operate, maintenance free, for as many as 30 years (according to the manufacturer's warranty). One of their features is a safety factor that may shut off the gas even though the piping is not damaged or leaking.

Electric seismic shut-off systems have recently been introduced. With sensors strategically placed in the building, they shut off the gas when a leak is detected. These systems need to be periodically tested and calibrated, and they need a maintained battery back-up, because often the first thing to go in an earthquake is electrical power.

Gas contractors can explain the features and limitations of available products. *(For recommended suppliers and installers, see Resources on our website, www.earthquakeprep.ca.)*

NATURAL GAS (METHANE) ALARMS

If you or a member of your family has concerns about your ability to smell natural gas, you may want to consider purchasing a natural gas (methane) alarm. These devices are available in most hardware and home supply stores. But they are not the same as, or a replacement for, carbon monoxide or smoke detectors *(which are covered in Section 19, Carbon Monoxide Poisoning).*

SECURING A NATURAL GAS WATER HEATER

One of your first priorities — now, before an earthquake — should be to restrain your water heater, whether it is gas-fired or electric. *(This procedure is fully explained in Section 12, Securing Your Home.)* When full, a water heater can weigh more than 180kg (400lbs). Because of its height and weight, even moderate ground movement can topple it, breaking gas or electrical connections and creating a dangerous situation as precious water from the tank and broken water lines floods your home. Gas water heaters are particularly vulnerable because they stand on feet that can collapse under abnormal strain.

> The British Columbia Building Codes require that service water heaters located in seismic velocity or acceleration zones 4, 5, or 6 shall be secured to the structure to prevent overturning.

SECURING OTHER APPLIANCES

Although less critical than your water heater, all other appliances should be anchored if possible. Once secured (but not before), gas appliances should be connected to the rigid piping by flexible metal connectors — by a professional. You will find anchoring instructions in *Section 12, Securing Your Home.*

Keep the areas in front of gas appliances clear of combustible materials such as laundry, paper, paints and solvents, charcoal, and propane cylinders. Do not store propane cylinders, lawnmowers, motorcycles, or other gasoline-powered vehicles indoors or near gas appliances.

> ACKNOWLEDGEMENT: Some of the information in this section is taken directly from the excellent booklets and leaflets published by BC Gas and is reproduced with the kind permission of BC Gas. For further information, visit their website, *www.bcgas.com*, or call their customer information line, 1-800 561-4427.

> DISCLAIMER: BC Gas makes clear in their literature that there is no way to forecast the intensity of and damage that might result from an earthquake, and that BC Gas is not liable for any damage or loss arising out of or in any way related to the information they present.

NATURAL GAS CHECKLIST

HOT WATER TANKS

> **Your hot water tank (gas or electric) is firmly secured** ☐
> *(see Section 12, Securing Your Home)*

APPLIANCES

> **Your other appliances are securely anchored** ☐
> *(see Section 12, Securing Your Home)*

GAS SHUT-OFF

> **You have a suitable wrench or shut-off tool in place** ☐
> **You have an earthquake-actuated automatic shut-off valve** ☐
> **or an electric seismic shut-off system installed**

REVIEW

ESCAPING GAS

> **Everyone in your household is familiar with:**
>
> - **how to detect and respond to escaping gas** ☐
> - **how to avoid causing an explosion** ☐
> - **when and how to turn off a gas supply** ☐
> - **when and how to turn off the gas supply to a particular appliance** ☐

REINSTATING A GAS SUPPLY

> **Everyone in your home knows that a gas supply should only be** ☐
> **reinstated by a qualified person — in normal times, a licenced gas fitter**

Disaster planning for pets is vital. Now is the time to make whatever arrangements you will want to have in place in a major crisis.

You should have — in each of the following locations — at least two weeks' reserves of food, water, and other necessities for every pet in your household:

WATER AND FOOD

- **a pet grab-and-go bag at home**, alongside your own bag *(see Section 15, Grab-and-go Bags)* — in case you have to leave home in a hurry with your pet. If you don't need to evacuate your home following the earthquake (or in any other emergency), these supplies will be there for you to draw on as your current supplies run out.

- **a grab-and-go bag in each vehicle in which a pet, such as a dog, may regularly travel** — in case you and your pet are caught away from home by the Big One (or any other disaster) and are unable to return home for an extended period.

Take the same care over any pet's drinking water as you will over your own *(see Section 4, Water)*. Do your best to keep pets from drinking water that may be contaminated.

If you can, continue to feed your pet the foods they are used to. If you feed canned food to dogs and cats, reduce the normal amount by half (supplementing with dry food) to reduce the possibility of the animal getting diarrhea. Have a can opener available — or buy flip-top cans. Store other foods in airtight plastic containers and rotate the contents every three months *(see Section 27, Check-ups)*.

Bear in mind that disposable bowls and mixing spoons don't have to be cleaned between uses.

Always keep a collar and tag on those animals that should normally wear collars. For a cat (even an indoor cat) use a breakaway collar that breaks apart if it gets caught.

IDENTIFICATION

Pets will be extremely disturbed by a major quake: they will bolt and hide if they possibly can. In the many weeks of confusion following the quake, they may or may not return of their own accord. Unidentified pets will be at greatest risk. In normal times, collars with ID tags, tattoos and imbedded chips are obvious ways of making it easier for a pet to be returned to you. After a major earthquake, however, when telephones and computers are unlikely to be working, a tag with your name, address, and telephone number on it may be your surest way of being reunited with a lost pet.

In your pet grab-and-go bags, keep some blank emergency ID tags (such as instantly laminated luggage labels) on which you can write your current whereabouts or any other information or instructions. Keep a ballpoint pen or indelible marker with the tags.

MISSING PETS

Now — while you have access to a photocopier — copy several dozen letter-size, "Lost pet" notices with a clear photograph and full description for each pet. Don't forget to mention a reward for your pet's safe return. Buy a roll of suitably sized, clear plastic bags in which to keep these signs dry and readable if you ever need to post them, and have thumb tacks, adhesive tape, or a staple gun (with enough staples) on hand. Leave space on these notices for further handwritten information (for example, how and where you can be contacted).

ABANDONING HOME

Create a couple of weatherproof notices that you will tack to your front and back doors if you have to vacate your home while a pet is still missing — a request for rescuers to look out for your pet. Describe the pet and leave space for a last-minute note of where you are headed or may be found.

Before leaving, put out lots of food and water. For cats, provide a box with a hole cut in it and a towel or small blanket with your, or the cat's, familiar scent on it — as a safe place for your cat to return to.

If you have a "Rescue my pet" emergency sticker on your door and your pet is with you when you leave, post a notice stating, "No pets here. I have my pet with me."

ALTERNATIVE LOCATIONS

Think of other possible locations where you might take your animals if you have to evacuate your home. These might include boarding kennels, veterinarian clinics with boarding space, grooming facilities, dog and cat clubs, and training clubs.

Pets (other than seeing-eye dogs and other recognized service dogs) will not be admitted to reception centres and emergency shelters — although, because of the numbers of displaced people who will have pets with them, rudimentary arrangements for pets may be created nearby.

SAFETY, COMFORT AND CONTROL

At any time, you should have a leash readily available for every dog you own but, because of the likelihood of dogs becoming terrified in the post-earthquake chaos and trying to slip their collars, consider having a harness as well as a leash in each dog's grab-and-go bag. And consider packing an extra leash (or suitable length of cord) for other dogs you may happen upon.

For cats, a harness will provide you with a measure of control and the cat with freedom to move about. Never leave a cat unattended while on a leash or in a harness; it might strangle itself.

Other options are plastic or collapsible wire carrying cages, waxed cardboard boxes, or compact fabric carrying bags. These come in a wide variety of designs, weights, and prices. Pack a pet towel or blanket for comfort and familiarity.

For each cat you will also want a small, lightweight litter box. And for every pet, don't forget to include toys and treats.

TETHERING

In a major quake, doors and windows may be broken and walls and fences may come down. For these and all sorts of other possible reasons, it may be necessary to restrict your dog's roaming, in which case a tethering stake and chew-proof cable or lightweight chain *(available from any large pet store)* might be the answer. When tethering a dog, be very aware of potential hazards (for example, the risk of the dog falling from an elevated porch or deck and hanging itself).

You would be wise to have a muzzle readily available for your dog in the uncertain days following a major quake. A muzzle will also be invaluable if a dog is injured and receiving first aid.

BUDDY SYSTEM

If someone watches your animals while you are on vacation, discuss a disaster plan. Consider coming to an arrangement with one or more of your pet-owning neighbours to look out for (and, if necessary, look after) each other's pets if one or more of you is incapacitated, cut off from home, or forced to leave before a pet has returned. Even in normal times, such an arrangement could save you (and them) heartache in a crisis situation (for example, if one of you is rushed to hospital or called out of town in a hurry).

Exchange updated files on your pets, along with feeding instructions, medical and vaccination records, details of tattoos or imbedded chips, recent photographs, your veterinarians' addresses and telephone numbers, and the names and telephone numbers of other friends or family members who are in your emergency plan.

VETERINARIAN'S PLANS

Ask at your veterinary clinic whether they have a disaster plan. If your regular vet does not have a plan, locate a veterinarian in your community who does. Knowing in advance where to take an injured or sick animal may save that animal's life — and save you considerable anxiety.

Have a permission slip put in your vet's file authorizing one or more of your buddies to obtain emergency treatment for your animal if you can't be reached.

Have a basic first aid kit and first aid book for your pet. You will find preassembled kits in most pet stores, or you can check with your vet to see what they recommend. If your own first aid kits are well stocked *(see Section 16, First Aid)*, you will already have most of what you might need right there.

If you have one or more birds, their first aid kit might include kwik stop or cornstarch to stop bleeding. Have heavy duty gloves available (for handling a bird or cat if it is injured), a long-handled net with small enough openings so that your bird cannot poke its head through, and/or a heavy towel in case your bird escapes and you have to recapture it. The heavy towel will also serve as a warm cover for a bird cage.

Keep your pet medical records in their home grab-and-go bag.

MEDICATIONS

Have at least two weeks' supply of any long-term medications — ideally, enough for a month or more. If a pet is on long-term medication, make a tag indicating this. Put it on your pet's collar.

BIRD CAGES

Bird cage doors and removable tops or bottoms should be secured to prevent them from opening during a disaster — and your bird escaping. You can use twist ties or metal ring closures to secure the cage. Keep wire (not galvanized) and a pair of pliers in your disaster supplies to make any necessary repairs to the cage.

HORSES AND LIVESTOCK

If you are responsible for horses and livestock, their food, water, medication, first aid and identification needs will be as great as those of your domestic pets and should be planned for ahead of time. If you have no identification on one of these larger animals, use a method that is not harmful yet fairly permanent (for example, an ID tag braided into a horse's mane).

The checklists below are designed for household pets, but they can be adapted to include horses and livestock.

ACKNOWLEDGEMENT: The above information is drawn in part from United Animal Nations' literature. You may wish to visit their web site (*www.uan.org*) or contact them at 916 429-2457. For more detailed life-saving tips for domestic animals, horses, and livestock, see *Out Of Harm's Way* by Terri Crisp, former Director of United Animal Nations' Emergency Animal Rescue Service.

PETS CHECKLIST

The checklists below cover the needs of a wide variety of household pets, from dogs, cats, rabbits, and hamsters to birds and reptiles. Please adapt and/or add to these lists as you see fit. If a pet doesn't need something (your tortoise doesn't need a harness, or your tarantula doesn't need a "Lost pet" kit), put an X in the relevant box.

    The first checklist below accommodates up to four different home grab-and-go bags, and the second checklist accommodates up to two different vehicle grab-and-go bags (you will need these only if you have one or more pets that regularly travel with you). While assembling the contents of any of these bags, consider weight. You will probably be carrying your own grab-and-go bag as well as your pet's bag *(see Section 15, Grab-and-go Bags)*.

HOME GRAB-AND-GO BAGS (PETS)

BAGS

suitable tote bag or backpack ☐☐☐☐

plastic bags
(for protecting contents of pack) ☐☐☐☐

waterproof label
(with your name, address, and telephone number) ☐☐☐☐

☐☐☐☐

WATER

small pack bottles (1 litre/34 oz) ☐☐☐☐
(see Section 4, Water)

lightweight water bowl ☐☐☐☐

☐☐☐☐

☐☐☐☐

PET FOOD
(cans and other containers should be of a one-feeding size, where possible, in order to avoid leftovers)

☐☐☐☐

☐☐☐☐

☐☐☐☐

☐☐☐☐

☐☐☐☐

UTENSILS

can opener □ □ □ □

lightweight food bowl □ □ □ □

disposable food bowls □ □ □ □

seed container □ □ □ □
(for a bird)

disposable spoons □ □ □ □
(to scoop and/or mix food)

IDENTIFICATION

pet is wearing a collar with name, address, and telephone tag □ □ □ □

spare breakaway collar □ □ □ □
(for a cat)

blank (emergency) ID tags □ □ □ □

photocopy of pet registration documents □ □ □ □

"Lost pet" kit □ □ □ □
(photocopied notices, plastic covers, thumb tacks, etc.)

ballpoint pen or indelible marker □ □ □ □

□ □ □ □

□ □ □ □

SAFETY, COMFORT AND CONTROL

leash and harness □ □ □ □
(for a dog or cat)

spare leash □ □ □ □

carrying cage □ □ □ □
(for any pet)

carrying bag □ □ □ □
(for a cat or small dog)

small blanket or suitable bedding □ □ □ □
(for any pet)

screw stake and chew-proof cable or chain
(for a dog)

muzzle
(for a dog)

lightweight litter box
(for a cat)

gravel
(for some birds)

heavy duty gloves
(for handling birds)

long-handled, small-mesh net
(for recapturing a bird)

heavy towel
(for recapturing a bird and/or covering cage)

FIRST AID

first aid kit

first aid book

pet medical records

MEDICATIONS

medical alert tag for pet's collar

OTHER PRECAUTIONS

buddy system in place ☐ ☐ ☐ ☐

pet files exchanged ☐ ☐ ☐ ☐

permission slip on file with veterinarian ☐ ☐ ☐ ☐

vet's disaster plans checked ☐ ☐ ☐ ☐

emergency boarding facility checked ☐ ☐ ☐ ☐

☐ ☐ ☐ ☐

☐ ☐ ☐ ☐

☐ ☐ ☐ ☐

HYGIENE

small plastic bags ☐ ☐ ☐ ☐
(invert and use as pooper-scoopers, as well as for general waste disposal)

antiseptic wipes ☐ ☐ ☐ ☐
(see Section 9, Sanitation)

hand disinfectant ☐ ☐ ☐ ☐
(see Section 9, Sanitation)

pre-moistened wipes ☐ ☐ ☐ ☐

small towels ☐ ☐ ☐ ☐

paper towels ☐ ☐ ☐ ☐

☐ ☐ ☐ ☐

☐ ☐ ☐ ☐

☐ ☐ ☐ ☐

MISCELLANEOUS

toys, treats, etc. ☐ ☐ ☐ ☐

inventory ☐ ☐ ☐ ☐
(an instant reminder of what is in this bag)

☐ ☐ ☐ ☐

VEHICLE GRAB-AND-GO BAGS (PETS)

BAG

    suitable tote bag or backpack ☐ ☐

    plastic bags ☐ ☐
    (for protecting contents of pack)

    waterproof label ☐ ☐
    (with your name, address, and telephone number)

    ☐ ☐

    ☐ ☐

WATER

    small pack bottles (1 litre/34 oz) ☐ ☐
    (see Section 4, Water)

    lightweight water bowl ☐ ☐

FOOD
(cans and other containers should be of a one-feeding size, where possible,
in order to avoid leftovers)

    ☐ ☐

    ☐ ☐

    ☐ ☐

    ☐ ☐

UTENSILS

    can opener ☐ ☐

    lightweight food bowl ☐ ☐

    disposable food bowls ☐ ☐

    disposable spoons ☐ ☐
    (to scoop and/or mix food)

    ☐ ☐

    ☐ ☐

    ☐ ☐

IDENTIFICATION

pet is wearing a collar with name, address, and telephone tag ☐☐

spare breakaway collar ☐☐
(for a cat)

blank (emergency) ID tags ☐☐

photocopy of pet registration documents ☐☐

"Lost pet" kit ☐☐
(photocopied notices, plastic covers, thumb tacks, etc.)

ballpoint pen or indelible marker ☐☐

☐☐

☐☐

☐☐

SAFETY, COMFORT AND CONTROL

leash and harness ☐☐
(for a dog or cat)

spare leash ☐☐

carrying cage ☐☐
(for any pet)

carrying bag ☐☐
(for a cat or small dog)

small blanket or suitable bedding ☐☐
(for any pet)

screw stake and chew-proof cable or chain ☐☐
(for a dog)

muzzle ☐☐
(for a dog)

lightweight litter box ☐☐
(for a cat)

☐☐

☐☐

FIRST AID

first aid kit

first aid book

MEDICATIONS

medical alert tag for pet's collar

HYGIENE

small plastic bags
(invert and use as pooper-scoopers, as well as for general waste disposal)

antiseptic wipes
(see Section 9, Sanitation)

hand disinfectant
(see Section 9, Sanitation)

pre-moistened wipes

small towel

paper towels

MISCELLANEOUS

toys, treats, etc.

inventory
(an instant reminder of what is in this bag)

The following excerpts are from *The Province's* two-day special of July 23-24, 2000 entitled "The Big One":

continued from page 172

continued from page 172

WHAT MAKES BC QUAKE?
THE AREA IS PRONE TO THREE DIFFERENT TYPES OF EARTHQUAKES:

1. Subduction earthquake. Also known as "the Big One"' Caused when the Juan de Fuca plate slides beneath the North American plate which we sit on. This could take place anywhere along the almost 1,000-kilometre-long junction of the two plates some 150 km off the west coast of Vancouver Island. Geological records show that over the last 5,000 years, about 14 subduction earthquakes have struck, averaging one every 500 years, but they have occurred as frequently as 200 years apart. The last one occurred at about 9:00 p.m. on January 26, 1700 and has been estimated at 9.2 on the Richter scale. This earthquake hits hardest on Vancouver Island, but unlike other earthquakes, affects a much larger area. Typically it takes the form of a long, low-frequency rolling of the earth, going on for three to four minutes and causing high-rise buildings, bridges and large buildings to sway or topple. Such an earthquake would cause moderate to major damage in many areas. The tsunami that would spring from it would likely arrive on the west coast of Vancouver Island in 10 to 15 minutes. The 1985 Mexico City earthquake, which killed at least 6,000 people and measured 8.1 on the Richter scale, led to numerous large buildings tumbling, even though the subduction earthquake that caused it occurred several hundred kilometres off shore.

2. North American plate earthquake. More common and potentially more deadly in a concentrated area are earthquakes occurring higher up in the crust on the North American plate. Their danger lies in their proximity to the surface — both the Lower Mainland and Vancouver Island sit on top of this plate. These earthquakes are characterized by violent, rapid shaking lasting for about 30 seconds. They affect a much smaller area and end relatively quickly, but much can happen. Kobe's 20-second earthquake in 1995, at 7.2 on the Richter scale, occurred very close to the surface and led to more than 6,000 deaths. Osaka, some 30 km away was hardly affected. That's the difference between Vancouver and Pitt Meadows. A large one causing some sort of structural damage can be expected every 10 years or so.

3. Juan de Fuca plate earthquake. This occurs at a greater depth than other earthquakes and is caused by pressure squeezing and buckling the plate which runs beneath the North American plate. At 50 km to 60 km, it originates much deeper than other earthquakes, but its position beneath our feet makes it potentially devastating. A particularly damaging one occurred beneath Seattle in 1965.[23]

Many of our familiar means of communicating with others will be wiped out in the first few seconds of a major earthquake.

TELEPHONES

During the quake itself, and during every significant aftershock, telephone receivers across the stricken region will leap off their hooks — many to be buried in fallen debris. The effect will be as if a million people tried to make telephone calls at the same time: the system will be swamped.

As the shaking ends and survivors pick themselves and others up, many will try to make calls — to friends, relatives, emergency services, utility companies, City Hall, or anyone. Within minutes, as radio and television stations around the world interrupt programs to announce a catastrophic earthquake in southwestern British Columbia and the Pacific Northwest of the United States, the outside world will attempt to call in — to find out what's happening, to speak to loved ones, to offer assistance. Almost none of these calls, wired (land-line) or wireless (cellular), will get through.

Here are some tips:

- **Get all telephones back on their hooks as soon as possible, or unplug them.**

- **Do not attempt to use a telephone immediately after the quake — unless a life is at stake.** Even then, you may be wasting valuable time. Telephone services will be disabled in the immediate aftermath of a major earthquake.

- **If you feel that you must try a call and there is no immediate dial tone, don't hang up.** Don't click the receiver button; simply wait on the line, hoping for a dial tone. If you cannot wait, hang up and go to a payphone, or the nearest fire, police, or ambulance station.

- **If you receive a dial tone and you delay in dialling, your call may be dropped from the network.** Have the telephone number that you are calling immediately available. If your call is dropped from the network, hang up for about 15 seconds and you may be able to use your telephone again.

- **To check whether your telephone circuit is busy or has been**

destroyed, blow into the receiver mouthpiece. If your telephone is connected to the wall jack and you can't hear yourself in the earpiece, the circuit is probably out of service and you will have to try another phone.

- **Payphones will likely be reconnected earlier than other lines.** Many, of course, will be damaged. Have rolls of quarters in your vehicle emergency kit and grab-and-go bags *(see Section 14, Vehicles and Section 15, Grab-and-go Bags)*. When you find a payphone that you can use, direct dial if possible. You may be able to use a calling card, Call-Me card, or prepaid phone card, but don't count on it: operators will be extremely busy.

- **Line priority in the first hours after a disaster will be given to emergency services, authorized government agencies, and private sector companies with what is called "essential line treatment."** They will be given a priority dial tone for outgoing calls.

- **Long-distance calls may go through when local calls don't —** because the telephone at the other end will be in working order.

- **Cellular phones may continue to operate, because they work through a system of multiple cell sites.** There will, however, be massive congestion problems. Save your battery: unless you have access to a vehicle and the right recharging cord, you may have no means of recharging it. And have times agreed with key people for when your cellphones will be switched on (for example, at 10 minutes after the hour and half-hour).

- **Damage to the telephone networks will be repaired on a priority basis.** It may be weeks or months before your telephone is working again.

OUT-OF-AREA CONTACT NUMBER

Everyone in your household should memorize the telephone number of an out-of-area friend or relative (preferably with voicemail or an answering machine) who lives at least 300 kms/200 miles away. This is the number that you will use — when telephoning becomes possible — to get word of your whereabouts and condition to loved ones, friends, and colleagues in the outside world, and to members of your household if you find yourselves separated by the quake.

Relatives and friends living outside southwestern British Columbia should also have this number securely noted — as a means of contact with you. You may have difficulty persuading them to take this matter seriously, but without such a contact number they may be among millions of people trying frantically and unsuccessfully to call into the stricken area.

As a back-up, memorize the non-emergency number of the police department wherever your main contact number is located.

Whatever numbers you choose, arrange to call again, if possible, at a specified time for another check-in. And ensure that your children know how to make long-distance and collect calls.

> ACKNOWLEDGEMENT: The above information is drawn in part from Telus's website, *www.telus.com*, which you can check for updated advice.

RADIOS

One of the first things you should do is listen to whatever emergency broadcasts may be on the air. The CBC's AM 690 and FM 105.7 stations are likely to be reliable sources of news and emergency information — assuming that their transmitters in Steveston, on Mt Seymour, and on the Malahat north of Victoria (all of which are dependent on the telephone infrastructure) are still functioning. Tune across the radio dial until you come to a station that is broadcasting news of the situation and possibly providing official announcements.

Remember, news gathering will be hampered by the disaster and initial reports from any source may be misleading. Rumours will abound.

Be sure to have one or more battery-powered or alternative-power radios distributed between your grab-and-go bags *(see Section 15, Grab-and-go Bags)*. Size and weight will be crucial. *(For recommended models and retailers, see Resources on our website, www.earthquakeprep.ca.)*

Here are some pointers:

- **Radios have two types of receiver:**

  AM/FM: These are the airwaves that carry your everyday listening. They are the ones that the government will use for emergency broadcasts.

  AM/FM/SW (shortwave): Shortwave signals circle the world and are primarily of value to people in remote spots (for example, at sea), or those who want to pick up remote stations (such as V*oice of America* and the BBC's *World Service*).

- **Portable radios are powered by:**

  batteries plus AC (with a jack that allows you to plug the radio into the wall); or

  alternative means, usually one or a combination of:

  — **a solar strip or panel** (that powers the radio in direct sunlight only)

  — **a crank** that winds a carbon steel spring or turns a generator that creates electricity that recharges a storage cell (sometimes with battery and AC options)

When looking at models with rechargeable batteries, bear in mind that NiCad batteries need to be treated and stored properly to work.

TWO-WAY RADIOS Two-way communication will be invaluable if you and your partner, family, or group need to split up. FRS (Family Radio Service) radios are compact, lightweight, and inexpensive. There are numerous models to choose between, costing from $50 Cdn a pair. They operate independently of the telephone network: usage is free and unlimited. You just turn on your unit, press the "talk" button, and start speaking — one person at a time.

The range of these radios is up to five kilometres in clear terrain, but much less in obstructed areas. Agree on times to call each other (such as 10 minutes after the hour and half-hour). Otherwise, keep your radio turned off to save batteries. Make sure that each radio is pre-set to the same channel and code — and mark each radio with the channel and code.

AMATEUR RADIO Many ham radio operators belong to their local emergency program. They have battery-powered radio communications equipment and will be acting as the eyes and ears of the stricken region, reporting on conditions to their regional emergency centre. Find the name and location of your nearest operator — and perhaps establish a connection ahead of time. In a crisis, he or she might be in position to relay information between you and the outside world.

WHISTLES A whistle could save your life. A good whistle carries much farther than the human voice and you can use one long after your ability to call out is exhausted. The elderly, infirm, children... any of us might need one and all of us should have several. Locate them in purses, on key chains, in your vehicle dash, on hooks close to your front and back doors — everywhere. Three short blasts is the recognized signal for help. *(For recommended models and retailers, see Resources on our website, www.earthquakeprep.ca.)*

MEGAPHONES Battery-powered megaphones start at about $150 Cdn. One of these loud-hailers could be essential if, for example, you live or work on an upper floor of a high-rise and might need to communicate with people in the street below or in a nearby building, or need to shout across any other wide divide.

BATTERY-POWERED STROBE LIGHTS These are the modern alternative to flares. Unlike flares, they offer no possibility of starting a fire or injuring someone. The flashing light may be visible for several miles, depending on weather conditions. The running time on one fresh D-cell battery is up to 72 hours. They are a great way of attracting attention.

These are a means of determining who is, or is not, accounted for at a disaster scene — a typed list of the names, unit or suite numbers, and telephone numbers of everyone living in the building, along with emergency contact names and numbers for those people. The occupants of multi-unit buildings should have one. So should every workplace with one or more employees. If a building has to be evacuated for any reason, rescuers may find such a list invaluable.

EMERGENCY ROLL-CALL AND CONTACT LISTS

Written messages will be an important part of post-earthquake communication. If you need to leave your home unoccupied, even for a short time, or if you abandon your vehicle to make your way home on foot, or if you arrive at a friend's or relative's home and find it empty, leave a prominently displayed note. Let people know whatever may be relevant, such as where you are heading and when or if you plan to return. Leave your full name, the time and the date — and make sure that others in your household know to do the same.

WRITTEN MESSAGES

You ought to have a set (or more) of these red "Help!" and green "Okay" signs *(available from survival equipment specialists)* to place in a prominent window (or windows) of your home to let rescuers know either that you need assistance or that they can focus their attention elsewhere.

"HELP!" AND "OKAY" SIGNS

In the chaotic aftermath of a major earthquake, think before rushing out impulsively to try to find or meet someone. The chances of your missing each other are enormous, and by being out at all you will be exposing yourself to risk.

As a precaution, however, agree with members of your household the routes that each of you will attempt to follow between, for example, school and home, workplace and home, downtown and home, the mall and home, and any other places that any of you frequent — if those distances are reasonably short. Keep these routes as simple as possible (for example, "Follow the north side of West Broadway as far as Trafalgar, then head directly home on the west side of Trafalgar. If West Broadway is blocked at any point, take the next street to the north of it, block by block until you can rejoin West Broadway. If Trafalgar is blocked at any point, take the next street west of it, block by block, until you can rejoin Trafalgar").

PRE-AGREED ROUTES

Plan primary and alternative meeting places (for example, a friend's home, a school, a church, a shopping mall) in case you are forced to evacuate your home before one or more of your household returns, or in case you find yourselves unable to return home, or you need to rendezvous with someone when either or both of your homes or

ALTERNATIVE REUNION PLACES

workplaces are inaccessible. This is especially relevant if you live or work in a potentially hazardous place (for example, close to a shoreline, oil refinery, major oil or gas pipeline, chemical site, electrical transmission towers, below a dam, or on low-lying land that might liquefy or flood in an earthquake).

Choose places that, if they are still standing, will offer shelter, the security of other people, and access to one or more payphones (see above). Agree on a time when you will try to be at the meeting place (for example, two hours after the earthquake) and where you will place (or hide) a message if you have to leave.

FAMILY PASSWORD

You might find it useful to establish an easily remembered password known only to you, your partner, your children, and any other authorized person. Without it, for example, your children would have reason to doubt someone who claims to have been sent by you to pick them up from school.

REGISTRATION AND REUNION SERVICE

In the weeks following a megaquake, the Canadian Red Cross will endeavour to put survivors in touch with relatives and friends, and vice versa, through their Registration and Inquiry (R & I) and Family Reunion services. In order to register, you will need to report to a reception centre. These will be set up in community centres, schools, church halls and similar buildings, depending on what buildings are left standing. You can find the planned locations by calling your local City Hall.

COMMUNICATIONS CHECKLIST

TELEPHONE CALLS

Everyone in your household knows what to expect of the telephone system in the aftermath of the Big One ☐

Everyone in your household has unopened rolls of telephone quarters in their:

- home grab-and-go bag ☐
- workplace grab-and-go bag ☐
- vehicle grab-and-go bag ☐

Everyone in your household has memorized a designated out-of-area contact number ☐

- selected number: (_____)_____
- contact name: _____

If your selected number is the number of a friend or relative, this person is aware of the role that he/she will be playing ☐

Your friends and relatives within and outside of southwestern British Columbia have this contact number securely noted ☐

Your friends and relatives understand that this is the number they should call following a major earthquake (or similar disaster) — even if they live just the other side of town from you ☐

RADIOS (AM/FM)

Everyone in your household has portable radios distributed between their:

- home grab-and-go bag ☐
- workplace grab-and-go bag ☐
- vehicle grab-and-go bag ☐

(Make sure that batteries are fresh, wrapped in plastic, and stored separately from but close to the radio.)

TWO-WAY RADIOS

Your household has an FRS (Family Radio Service) walkie-talkie in each of your:

- home grab-and-go bags ☐
- workplace grab-and-go bags ☐
- vehicle grab-and-go bags ☐

(Make sure that batteries are fresh, wrapped in plastic, and stored separately from the radio.)

WHISTLES

Everyone in your household has a whistle in their:

- home grab-and-go bag ☐
- workplace grab-and-go bag ☐
- vehicle grab-and-go bag ☐

MEGAPHONES

If one or more of these might be relevant in your situation, you have one:

- at home ☐
- at work ☐
- in your vehicle ☐
- at your cottage or on your boat ☐

BATTERY-OPERATED STROBE LIGHTS

If one or more of these might be relevant in your situation, you have one:

- at home ☐
- at work ☐
- in your vehicle ☐
- at your cottage or on your boat ☐

EMERGENCY ROLL-CALL OR CONTACT LIST

If applicable, you have an up-to-date list:

- of tenants and/or owners in your multi-unit building ☐
- of employees in your workplace ☐

WRITTEN MESSAGES

Everyone in your household understands the importance of leaving prominently displayed, clearly worded, written messages behind when:

- leaving your home unoccupied ☐
- abandoning a vehicle ☐

"HELP!" AND "OKAY" SIGNS

You have one or more sets of these:

- at home ☐
- at work ☐
- in your vehicle ☐
- at your cottage or on your boat ☐

AMATEUR RADIO OPERATORS:

You have located (and possibly introduced yourself to)
one or more nearby ham radio operators _____ ☐

EMERGENCY ROUTES

Everyone in your household has agreed on which routes you may attempt to
follow between regularly frequented places such as: _____ ☐

- _____ and _____
- _____ and _____
- _____ and _____
- _____ and _____

ALTERNATIVE REUNION PLACES

Everyone in your household and other relevant persons have agreed where
you will attempt to meet if you are separated from your home or each other,
or are unable to make it to your normal meeting place. _____ ☐

- reunion place #1 _____
- reunion place #2 _____
- reunion place #3 _____
- reunion place #4 _____

You have established places (possibly concealed) in each of the above
locations where you will leave a message if you have to leave early _____ ☐

FAMILY PASSWORD

Everyone in your household and other relevant persons have agreed on
the word you will use to establish the credibility of anyone claiming to
be sent by someone else in your household _____ ☐

REUNION SERVICES

Everyone in your household is aware that the Canadian Red Cross will be
attempting to put survivors and relatives in touch with each other in the
weeks following a major earthquake or other disaster, and that their
Registration and Inquiry (R & I) and Family Reunion services will be
located in emergency reception centres: _____ ☐

- reception centre #1 _____
- reception centre #2 _____

The following excerpts are from an article in *The Globe and Mail* of April 20, 2001:

The discovery of previously undetected subterranean movements under the southern end of Vancouver Island has increased concern about earthquake hazards along the West Coast.

In an article published today in *Science* magazine, scientists from the Geological Survey of Canada say the movements may increase stresses in the Earth's crust that could lead to an earthquake comparable to the 9.5-magnitude quake that hit Chile in 1960, one of only two events of that size in 100 years of global earthquake records....

Seismologist Alison Bird said the research... does not require authorities to revise thir recommendations to British Columbians.... "Everyone should already be taking measures to prepare for the Big One," she said. Although it may not come for years, a major earthquake could happen at any time.... "People should be prepared, as if it was going to happen tomorrow."

Scientists had previously believed the Juan de Fuca plate under the Strait of Juan de Fuca was gradually moving under the North American plate, pushing the West Coast eastward by a few millimetres each year.... However, computer analysis of the 1999 movements in the fall of 2000 detected motion in the reverse direction for almost two weeks. The scientists now believe the North American plate is moving in spurts or discrete pulses, a step east, followed by a much smaller retreat to the west, then another move to the east.

Each spurt, which is called a silent deep-slip event, could bring a major earthquake closer.[24]

Section 23
DOCUMENTATION

Here are some suggestions for ways of having essential information where you need it, when you need it. These precautions could prove invaluable at any time!

Consider issuing several of these laminated cards to every member of your household. Each person's cards should bear the following information:

LAMINATED DISASTER PLAN CARDS

- **name**

- **photo ID (a small headshot)**

- **home address**

- **home telephone number**

- **date of birth**

- **blood type**

- **any pertinent medical information**

- **out-of-area contact number**
  (see Section 22, Communications)

- **alternative meeting places**
  (see Section 22, Communications)

- **telephone number (if any) for alternative meeting place**
  (see Section 22, Communications)

If you are taking this seriously, you will carry these cards in wallets, purses, fanny packs, hip pockets, vehicle glove compartments, and every one of your grab-and-go bags. Why? As an always-present means of identification.

Imagine — immediately following the main quake, you are found, away from home, injured and unconscious. With clear identification, you will be reunited with your family or familiar surroundings as rapidly as circumstances allow. Without such identification, people are going to be worrying unnecessarily about you.

Again, imagine — you are out hiking when the quake hits. By the time you reach home on foot, many hours later, the area surrounding your home has been cordoned off because of a major gas leak, fire, or other danger. Emergency services personnel (or your neighbourhood emergency preparedness team) are refusing entry to unauthorized persons. Plausible identification may come in handy.

LAMINATED EMERGENCY NUMBER CARDS

Secure a laminated card with key telephone numbers on it close to each of your telephones. Include numbers for Emergency Services, Poison Control, BC Gas, BC Hydro, your workplace, school and/or daycare, neighbours, friends, and relatives (using their first names only). Include area codes.

Why laminated? Because they will stand up to wear and tear better that way and still be legible in the aftermath of an earthquake.

PHOTOCOPIES OF YOUR PLASTIC CARDS

Have you ever lost a credit card? Or a whole wallet full of cards? Know the feeling? Make an up-to-date, photocopied record of all of your cards — driver's licence, VISA, MasterCard, social insurance, health, the Bay, library, etc. The day you lose any of these, you will have exact details on hand and be in position to cancel immediately — especially if you have taken the precaution of writing the lost card or cancellation telephone numbers against each card. Keep these records in a fireproof container. Ensure that others in your household do the same.

PHOTOGRAPHIC AND VIDEO RECORDS

Photograph and/or video the exterior and interior of your home, in detail, including the contents of closets, cupboards, drawers, boxes, garages, etc. Photograph and/or video your vehicle and any other assets, such as livestock, motorhomes, or boats. You will be building clear evidence of your possessions and the way your home looked at a certain date. This record will form the basis for an inventory if you ever need one for insurance purposes, or for any other reason. Keep this evidence in a fireproof container.

ONE-TIME USE CAMERA

These can be really handy for recording damage, etc. As a precaution, I keep one in the dash of my car. Note the expiry date on the camera in your diary. What's wrong with your ordinary camera? Nothing, probably, but it may not have film (or a full film) in it when you need it, or someone may have borrowed it — who knows?

COMPUTER DATA BACK-UP

Do you faithfully, frequently, regularly back up all of your data? If you don't, your computing life is likely to be ruined long before the Big One does it for you! Your back-up needs to be safely stored, preferably in a fireproof container.

RECEIPTS AND WARRANTY FILE

Set up a file for receipts, warranties, and serial numbers of all significant purchases. This could be as simple as a large manila envelope or as sophisticated as a ring binder with plastic insert pages. When your juicer breaks down, you will know exactly where to look for the warranty and receipt. If the Big One junks just about everything you have, there will be a record of much of what you lost. Keep this information in your fireproof container *(available from office supply stores.)*

Before an earthquake, decisions about seismic upgrade requirements, including financing, are extraordinarily difficult. After the earthquake, every property owner wishes he or she had done more.

Mr Eadie,
a Project Manager of the City of Santa Cruz Redevelopment Agency, at the time of the 1989 Loma Prieta Earthquake

DOCUMENTATION CHECKLIST

LAMINATED DISASTER PLAN CARDS

Everyone in your household has a number of these distributed ☐
between wallets, purses, hip pockets, glove compartments, fanny packs, etc.

LAMINATED EMERGENCY NUMBER CARDS

You have a card secured close to each of your telephones ☐

PHOTOCOPIES OF PLASTIC CARDS

Everyone in your household has a photocopied record of all of their ☐
plastic cards, along with lost card or cancellation telephone numbers

These records are securely stored ☐

PHOTOGRAPHIC/VIDEO RECORDS

You have a detailed photographic and/or video record of the ☐
interior and exterior of your home, vehicle, and any other assets

These records are securely stored ☐

ONE-TIME USE CAMERA

You (and others in your household) have one or more of these
distributed between:

- your home ☐
- your workplaces ☐
- your vehicles ☐
- your grab-and-go bags ☐

COMPUTER DATA BACK-UP

You have a frequent, regular computer back-up system in place ☐

Your back-up files are securely stored ☐

RECEIPTS AND WARRANTIES FILE

You have a file set up to hold all of your significant ☐
warranties, receipts and serial numbers

This file is securely stored ☐

Section 24
INSURANCE

W E KNOW THAT A MEGAQUAKE IS GOING to happen at some point and yet many of us don't have earthquake insurance.

Earthquake coverage is available as a simple endorsement (add-on) to your homeowner's policy, condominium package, or tenant's contents policy. A homeowner can calculate the approximate cost of this cover by taking the value of their home (say $200,000), multiplying that by 70 per cent to obtain the notional contents value (in this case, $140,000), adding the two amounts together (to make $340,000), and multiplying this figure by 0.0007 (to reach an earthquake cover premium of $238).

A condominium owner or a tenant can calculate the approximate cost of earthquake cover for the contents of their home by taking the contents replacement value (say, $50,000) and multiplying it by 0.0006 (to reach an earthquake premium of $30 that will be added to their base rate).

Typically, there will be a deductible of 5-10 per cent. This means that the owner of a $400,000 home will have to pay $20,000 to $40,000 of any earthquake-related claim before the insurance company pays anything. Likewise, on a $50,000 contents policy, a condo owner or tenant will have to pay the first $2,500 to $5,000. That may not be a comfortable prospect, but being caught with no coverage at all would indeed be grim.

Here are some important points:

- **fire following an earthquake**
  Make sure that your policy covers fires started as a result of an earthquake.

- **temporary living expenses**
  If you are forced to abandon your home as a result of an earthquake, this coverage will pay your living expenses over and above those you would normally incur — mainly accommodations and meals. There is usually no deductible on this coverage.

- **explosions and floods**
  These are perils that your home insurance will not cover.

- **insurance industry's ability to pay**
  The insurance industry has made significant strides towards

ensuring that they will be able to meet the gigantic losses incurred in the event of a major earthquake.

• **government compensation**
If you think the government might pay compensation, visit the Provincial Emergency Program's web site, *www.pep.bc.ca*. You will see that, while Disaster Financial Assistance (DFA) provides assistance for homeowners, renters, small business owners, farmers, and charitable and non-profit organizations in some disaster scenarios, it does not cover loss or damage to items for which insurance was reasonably and readily available.

Earthquake insurance (with coverage for fire following the earthquake and temporary living expenses) could prove to be the difference between your life being badly disrupted and completely ruined. Think of it as a must. If you are already insured, check the terms of your coverage. Otherwise, contact a reliable insurance broker. *(For the name of a recommended broker, see Resources on our website, www.earthquakeprep.ca.)*

INSURANCE CHECKLIST

EARTHQUAKE INSURANCE

You have coverage (including fire following an earthquake and temporary living expenses) on your:

• **home** _____ ☐
• **business** _____ ☐
• **cottage or boat** _____ ☐

Tthe following precautions are difficult to categorize, but nonetheless important.

Everyone in your household who wears eye glasses or contact lenses should have at least one spare pair — especially if they would be severely incapacitated without them. In the aftermath of the Big One, there will be no going around to your local optician for a quick replacement. Store spares securely at home, and possibly at work and in your vehicle.

SPARE EYEGLASSES/ CONTACT LENSES

    Anyone who depends on glasses or contact lenses should keep them overnight in a strong case in a drawer of their night-table, in a strong case hanging from a hook, or wherever else they stand some chance of finding them once the shaking stops.

I recommend that you get into the habit of securing anything and everything — keys, wallets, purses, etc. — that you will want to find easily and immediately after an earthquake. Keeping these things in a drawer is one possibility, but drawers are likely to fly all over the place. Another is to use deep hooks — the kind that will hold a hanging item in place through the most violent shaking. You won't want to be hunting for keys or any other essentials in the debris of a major quake.

SECURING THINGS

> If you lock a sliding patio or balcony door in a partially open position, keep the key on a deep hook where you will immediately be able to find it, even in darkness. That door may be your only means of escape in an emergency.

Everyone in earthquake country should keep a pair of thick-soled shoes beside or under their bed. We are all going to be walking over broken glass and sharp debris for weeks to come. If the Big One happens in the night, almost the first thing that you will want to do is put on a sturdy pair of shoes. Try to imagine the problems that will face the hundreds of thousands of people who won't follow this advice.

THICK-SOLED SHOES

    Shoes kept in a plastic bag or shoebox with the lid lightly taped on with (easily broken) masking tape may be more easily found and less likely to be filled with debris.

CASH RESERVES

You will need a reserve of coins and small denomination notes (at least $100 per person, if you can afford it). Keep the money in a sealed envelope: no dipping! Automated cash dispensing machines will almost certainly be inoperable following a major quake; banks will be closed; and debit cards, credit cards, and cheques may not be accepted.

PAYPHONE CHANGE

In addition to your cash reserves, you should have at least $20 in quarters for you and your household. Payphones may be working (or eventually start working) when other lines are still restricted or unavailable *(see Section 22, Communications)*. You will also need rolls of quarters at work *(see Section 13, Workplaces)* and in one or more of your grab-and-go bags *(see Section 15, Grab-and-go Bags)*.

DOWNED OR EXPOSED ELECTRICAL WIRES

Wherever there are downed or exposed electrical wires, treat them as being energized (live). Use "Caution" or "Do Not Enter" barricade tape *(see Section 11, Tools)* or home-made string and cardboard "Danger" signs to cordon off the area to a distance of at least 10 metres (33 feet).

SPECIAL NEEDS

Consider the needs of any infants, young children, seniors, people with disabilities, or others in your home, and in any other area of your responsibility. Who, for example, is dependent on items such as dentures, hearing aids, pacemakers, mobility aids, or essential medications? Who will be looking out for these people — and do they know that they have a support team?

A major earthquake and its aftermath will be especially frightening for children: they are likely to need all of the reassurance, tenderness, additional attention, and inclusion you can give them.

Knowing that the needs of those who are particularly vulnerable will be met is a crucial aspect of your overall preparations.

If you are disabled, fragile, or have special needs, now is the time to take precautions regarding your own safety and survival in a crisis situation. For example:

- **assess your special needs**
  Write them down — then communicate them to those close to you.

- **safe places**
  Keep medications (with duplicate prescriptions) and any special equipment you require in safe places where you can easily reach them.

- **scoop bag**
  Consider having a cloth string bag on hand into which you can quickly scoop essentials (for example, your glasses, small purse, and medications), if necessary.

- **be familiar with this guide**

  If, for example, there is a need to evacuate your home, you will be as much in need of a well-equipped grab-and-go bag as anyone else. You are more likely than most to be vulnerable to carbon monoxide poisoning and should take precautions, if these are not already in place. You may find it particularly valuable to have a whistle close by at all times with which to attract attention in any emergency. Take whatever precautions make sense for you.

HALF-FULL GAS TANK

If you make a habit of always keeping your vehicle gas tank at least half full, an earthquake (or other emergency) won't catch you with your tank close to empty. Gas stations are likely to be crippled in a major earthquake, and any that remain intact and open will be sold out of gas (and just about everything else) within minutes.

CLEARLY NUMBERED HOME

Have you ever wondered how pizza delivery drivers, let alone emergency services, spot the semi-invisible numbers on most homes? Your home should be easily identified at any time, including in the middle of the night, in a hydro outage, or in the wake of the Big One, when there will be fallen trees and debris everywhere. Make sure that your home can be easily identified from both the street and any back lane.

BABY-SITTERS

Are your baby-sitters (if you have them) clear on what to do during and immediately following an earthquake? Probably not! You could do worse than give them the relevant portions of this guide to read. Thoroughly quiz them (and quiz them again a week or two later, and again a month or two later). Then reward them if they "pass."

MUTUAL AID PLANS

Earthquake damage can vary considerably within a neighbourhood, a city, or between cities. Typically, there will be pockets of severe destruction and pockets that are relatively unscathed. Come to an arrangement with friends, relatives, and neighbours that you will be there for each other in the event of one (or more) of your homes becoming uninhabitable.

QUAKEALERT ALARM

For the household or workplace that already has everything, you might want to add the finishing touch, a QuakeAlert alarm — a conversation piece if ever there were one. This compact, wall-mounted alarm provides from ten seconds to two minutes audible warning of an earthquake above magnitude 5.0. It picks up the primary P-waves that precede the slower-moving but damaging S-waves and the even more damaging R-waves. That warning could provide you with the extra moments needed to reach an ideal position in which to ride out the quake. The alarm has already proven itself invaluable in warning rescuers of aftershocks — allowing them to get clear of the partially collapsed structures in which they were working. *(For recommended retailers, see Resources on our website, www.earthquakeprep.ca.)*

INCLUDE EVERYONE
Make sure that everyone in your household of school age or older is familiar with where everything is and knows what needs to be done. They may be at home when disaster strikes, while you are trapped on the other side of town. Include children, especially — properly handled, they will be thrilled to be involved and treated as totally responsible. Rehearsals may feel a bit silly at this point, but then so can fire drills and all sorts of other wise precautions. Familiarity and practise will go a long way to increasing everybody's ability to handle the situation if — or when — it happens. Include your neighbours. Show them this guide. Let them know of your intention to become fully prepared. Encourage them to do the same. Their being adequately prepared may make all the difference to you.

SMART TIPS CHECKLIST

SPARE EYEGLASSES/CONTACT LENSES

Everyone in your household who needs glasses or contact lenses has at least one (current prescription) pair in place: _____ ☐

Name: _____ Location: _____

Name: _____ Location: _____

Name: _____ Location: _____

Name: _____ Location: _____

Name: _____ Location: _____

Name: _____ Location: _____

THINGS SECURED

Everyone in your household is aware of the importance of _____ keeping items (such as keys, purses, etc.) where they can immediately be found in the aftermath of a big quake ☐

THICK-SOLED SHOES

Everyone in your household is in the habit of keeping a pair of _____ thick-soled shoes beside or under their bed ☐

CASH RESERVES

You have a sealed cash reserve in place for your household _____ ☐
Total cash reserve: $_____

PAYPHONE CHANGE

In addition to your cash reserve (*see above*), you have _____ at least $20 in quarters for your household ☐

Total quarters reserve: $_____

DOWNED OR EXPOSED ELECTRICAL WIRES

Everyone in your household is aware of the danger posed by _____ downed or exposed wires and what to do in such a situation ☐

SPECIAL NEEDS

The special needs of everyone in your household (and/or other areas of responsibility) have been assessed and addressed ☐

HALF-FULL GAS TANK

Your vehicle gas tank is unlikely to be allowed to fall below half full ☐

CLEARLY NUMBERED HOME

Your home is clearly numbered (front and back) ☐

BABY-SITTERS

Your regular baby-sitters are earthquake briefed ☐

MUTUAL AID PLANS

You have one or more of these in place ☐

QUAKEALERT ALARM

You have one of these installed in:

- your home ☐
- your workplace ☐

INCLUSION

Everyone in your household is well-informed and well-rehearsed on most aspects of your emergency precautions ☐

Τ HE BC FIRE ACT REQUIRES SCHOOLS TO have fire emergency plans in place, but there is currently no legislation covering earthquake preparedness. It is up to school boards and schools themselves to decide the levels of funding and priority they will ascribe to disaster response and emergency management. Standards of earthquake/emergency preparedness in daycares, pre-schools, schools, and colleges in British Columbia therefore vary considerably. A few are excellent, some are adequate, but most are culpably inadequate. Your responsibility as a parent is to be satisfied about the arrangements where your child goes to school.

GOVERNMENT INITIATIVES

The Provincial Emergency Program (PEP), in partnership with the Ministry of Education, is developing a program that will encourage BC youth to make emergency preparedness part of their lifestyle — to develop safe life practices that will stay with them forever. This is likely to be no more than a long overdue set of guidelines, but it will be a mighty step in the right direction. And the Seismic Mitigation Branch of the Ministry of Finance is working to increase safety in provincially owned school facilities during an earthquake.

If the Big One can hold off for a decade or two longer, there may come a time when schools' lack of preparedness is a thing of the past — but we can't count on the Juan de Fuca and North American plates staying locked that long. *(For further information, visit the School Protection Program website, www.bcspp.org/index.shtml, and the Provincial Emergency Program's website, www.pep.bc.ca.)*

YOUR INITIATIVES

If there is a well-established program at your child's school, you will already know all about it. You will know what has been done to upgrade facilities and what is planned; what equipment and supplies are securely stored on site; what procedures the children and staff will follow; and what will be expected of you. If you are in this category, you are fortunate.

If you feel that the arrangements in your underfunded, overstretched school are less than adequate, it may be pressure from you that helps this priority gain a firmer footing on the school board's vast list of priorities. One obvious way of doing this is through your Parent Advisory Committee (PAC) or School Planning Council (SPC). The more proactive a school's PAC or SPC, the more likely a school is to be prepared. If your committee or council is dismissive on this subject — after all, many people really don't believe that a major earthquake is likely, or that it will be nearly as devastating as it will be — you might present them with well-selected, photocopied pages from this book.

> School District No. 46 (Sunshine Coast) and the district PACs are doing a remarkable job of getting their 10 elementary and 3 secondary schools earthquake/emergency prepared. They are on their way to having a secured shipping container stocked with all manner of emergency supplies on each of their school grounds, and having well thought-out school emergency plans. This initiative, which has included fundraising and grants, originated with a handful of staff and parents and is an example of what can be done when parents and a school board work together.

BRIEFING YOUR CHILD   Whatever the arrangements are (or aren't) at your school, thoroughly brief your child yourself. Your child needs to know exactly what to expect and do if a major earthquake or other disaster strikes while he or she is on the way to school, at school, or or on the way home from school. If the school does not have arrangements in place for these and other eventualities, you may have to come up with arrangements and agreements of your own. Under the Schools Act, teachers are responsible for the children in their care during school hours. That presumably means that, if the Big One happens while your child is at school, the staff will stand by the children at least until the time school normally closes. What happens then is anyone's guess. The staff will be under huge pressure to leave for their own homes and loved ones — and they will be surrounded by children, some of whom may not be picked up for days.

If the telephone system is down, as it almost certainly will be, you will have no means of communicating with the school or your child. You could be anywhere when the Big One hits, including on the wrong side of collapsed bridges. You could be injured. Whatever your situation, until you are reunited with your child, he or she will be dependent on the school's emergency procedures and any pre-arranged plans of yours.

Arrange for one or more neighbours or other parents to pick up your child if, in a disaster, it seems unlikely that you will be able to do it yourself. And instruct your child on what to do if an authorized pick up doesn't happen and remaining at the school becomes impossible or ceases to be the smart thing to do.

Having your child familiar with what to expect in a major quake and how to handle him or herself in the hours immediately following the quake will go a long way towards alleviating stress for both of you. The purpose of this preparation is not to scare your child, but rather to make earthquake planning a matter-of-fact part of their life.

Ideally, every child would have a school grab-and-go bag *(see Section 15, Grab-and-go Bags)* — something manageable, but a lot more useful than the current, extremely limited "comfort kits." These bags would be kept in each child's locker at school — except that I understand children don't normally have a locker until they reach secondary school. An alternative would be for grab-and-go bags to be stored in secure locations around the school, or in one or more secure containers on the school grounds. It would take just a bit of determination on the part of parents to have this inexpensive step happen — and one way of raising money for it, or for anything else, would be selling copies of this guide as a fundraiser.

GRAB-AND-GO BAGS

SCHOOL EMERGENCY PLAN REVIEW

You and your child are familiar with:

the school emergency preparedness procedures ☐

the terms on which your child will be released from school following ☐
a major earthquake or other disaster

You have an arrangement in place whereby:

one or more pre-authorized adults (such as a neighbour or another ☐
parent with whom your child feels comfortable) are briefed to pick up
your child if it seems unlikely that you will be able to do so yourself

You and your child are agreed on:

what your child should do if caught between home and school ☐
when a major earthquake or other disaster strikes

a set of fall-back agreements — plans of your own that your child fully ☐
understands and will follow under agreed circumstances,
such as the school becoming an unsafe place to stay

"When the wind blows," goes an old Japanese saying, "coopers get rich" (*kaze ga fuku to okeya ga moukaru*). Why do coopers get rich? Because when the wind blows it throws dust into people's eyes. Some people go blind and, having nothing better to do once blind, they take up the *shamisen* (a Japanese stringed instrument). This leads to a decrease in the cat population, since *shamisen* strings are made of cat-gut. With no cats around, rats proliferate and gnaw incessantly on wooden barrels. Thus new barrels have to be made. Thus coopers get rich.

This obscure logic has a very simple element of truth: that a single event can lead to the most unexpected consequences. The scale and scope of consequences from an earthquake are potentially enormous.[25]

Section 27
CHECK-UPS

THERE ARE THINGS THAT MUST BE checked or reviewed on a regular basis. Put reminders in your diary or organizer for all of the reviews below that apply to you and/or your household. Try to undertake check-ups at the beginning of each month. That way, when the first of each month comes around you will know that something needs to be done.

CHECK-UPS REVIEW

In the boxes on the right, enter the date of your most recent review.

EVERY MONTH

Fire extinguishers
— check gauges:
- in your home
- in your workplace
- in your vehicle

Smoke and carbon monoxide detectors
— test alarm:
- in your home
- in your workplace

EVERY THREE MONTHS

Home-bottled drinking water reserves
— rotate or replace as necessary:
- in your home
- in your grab-and-go bag
- in your workplace
- in your vehicle

Emergency food reserves (other than canned)
— rotate or replace as necessary:
- in your home
- in your grab-and-go bag
- in your workplace
- in your vehicle

Medications
— rotate or replace as necessary:
- in your home
- in your grab-and-go bag

Pet food (other than canned)
— rotate or replace as necessary:
- in pet's home grab-and-go bag
- in pet's vehicle grab-and-go bag

EVERY SIX MONTHS

Water cooler drinking water reserves
— rotate or replace as necessary:

- in your home ⬚
- in your workplace ⬚
- in your vehicle ⬚

Emergency food reserves (including canned)
— rotate or replace as necessary:

- in your home ⬚
- in your grab-and-go bag ⬚
- in your workplace ⬚
- in your vehicle ⬚

Pet food (including canned)
— rotate or replace as necessary:

- in pet's home grab-and-go bag ⬚
- in pet's vehicle grab-and-go bag ⬚

Flashlight and electric lantern batteries
— replace:

- in your home ⬚
- in your grab-and-go bag ⬚
- in your workplace ⬚
- in your vehicle ⬚

Radio batteries
— replace:

- in your home ⬚
- in your grab-and-go bag ⬚
- in your workplace ⬚
- in your vehicle ⬚

Smoke and carbon monoxide detector batteries
— replace:

- in your home ⬚
- in your workplace ⬚

**Any other time-sensitive or perishable items
— rotate or replace as necessary:**
- in your home ☐
- in your grab-and-go bag ☐
- in your workplace ☐
- in your vehicle ☐

Review all checklist entries ☐

Re-assess your overall state of readiness ☐
(What changes have there been in your circumstances? New pet?
Child left home? Revised school emergency preparedness plans?
Changes in medications? Change of vehicle?)

**Household update: if you live with others, hold one
or more refresher sessions with everyone concerned** ☐
(Quiz each other. It is the only way to keep your minds fresh on the
things that you must know and be able to recall in the heat of the
moment. Rehearse taking cover — again — in all sorts of different
situations. If the Big One happens in the next few minutes, are you
ready? What will you do as soon as the shaking stops? And after that?
Will you be self-sufficient and in a position to help others, or will you
be part of the problem?)

EVERY TWO YEARS

**Small pack drinking water reserves
— rotate or replace as necessary:**
- in your home ☐
- in your grab-and-go bag ☐
- in your workplace ☐
- in your vehicle ☐

Section 28
WARNINGS

T HERE ARE NUMEROUS THINGS THAT WE should be aware of and cautious about in daily life and, particularly, in emergency situations. Many of them are covered in this guide. Here are some specific reminders:

Store toxic and flammable materials (petroleum products, chemicals, oil-based paint, stains, and varnishes; cleaning fluids, turpentine, mineral spirits, and other solvents; fertilizers, camping stove fuels, and charcoal-lighter fluid; etc.) in small quantities in their original containers or in approved safety containers:

STORAGE OF HAZARDOUS MATERIALS

- **in one or more secure, cool, dry spots away from living areas**

- **as close to the ground as possible, in buckets, boxes, or cabinets securely fastened to a wall or floor (or otherwise located where they cannot spill)**

- **below 40°C (104°F)**

- **away from open flames and other heat sources (such as your furnace, boiler, or hot water heater), including sunlight**

- **away from rain, and food and water reserves**

Plug cylinder outlets when tanks are not connected for use. Never store flammable liquids in glass jars, which break easily.

Rags soaked in oils or paint thinners will burn if exposed to flame. Dispose of such rags immediately after use, hang them outdoors to dry (or "harden"), or store them in a sealed metal container.

Treat gasoline with extreme caution: its vapours can be ignited by the smallest spark. Never smoke near gasoline.

Potentially deadly combinations (such as ammonia and chlorine) should be kept well away from each other. Treat all such substances with care. *(For retailers of large, metal boxes that would be ideal for storage purpose, see Resources on our website, www.earthquakeprep.ca.)*

CO poisoning can kill — very easily, without the victim being aware that it is happening. Many people are unaware of how dangerous it can be to use fuel-burning appliances (camping stoves, portable heaters, etc.) in confined spaces with inadequate ventilation. These are the conditions in

CARBON MONOXIDE POISONING

which many of us will want to cook and keep warm in the aftermath of a winter earthquake. Deaths will, unfortunately, occur.

Remember, there is a risk of carbon monoxide poisoning with the use of any combustible material. *(Please read and understand Section 19, Carbon Monoxide Poisoning.)* Your life and the lives of others may depend on your being aware of this risk. Have fire extinguishers on hand; wrap up well; and allow plenty of ventilation.

OPEN FLAMES AND APPLIANCES

Never leave any open flame or lit appliance unattended or fall asleep while any kind of flame or appliance is lit. Accidents happen. Screen fireplace fires to prevent sparks igniting anything in the room. Bear in mind that candles can topple and candles and tealights can leak. In emergency situations these should be used on a bed of aluminium foil. And always ensure that there is adequate ventilation.

WOOD-BURNING STOVES AND FIREPLACES

These rely on fully functioning flues and chimneys which are likely to be damaged in a major earthquake — eliminating this means of cooking and/or heating for you until the problem has been satisfactorily fixed. It is vital that flues and chimneys be swept at least once a year in order to avoid build-up of waste materials which can allow smoke and gases (including deadly carbon monoxide) to enter the room where the fire is burning.

AVOIDING GAS AND OTHER EXPLOSIONS

Following an earthquake, do not use matches, smoke a cigarette, use a regular flashlight or operate any switch or electrical appliance until you are sure that there are no gas leaks or spills of flammable liquids. If investigating for natural gas leaks or spills of flammable liquids, use an intrinsically safe flashlight or a lightstick *(see Section 20, Natural Gas)*.

SIPHONING GAS

Never siphon gasoline by mouth. If you need to siphon gas — for example, to fuel a chainsaw or to transfer gas from one vehicle to another — use a multi-use siphon pump *(see Section 14, Vehicles)*.

GASOLINE-POWERED GENERATORS

Always operate a generator outdoors, well away from doors and windows. Connect lights and appliances directly to the generator. If an extension cord must be used, ensure that it is a properly rated, CSA (Canadian Standards Association) approved cord. Direct installation of a generator to an existing electrical system should only be done by a qualified technician.

Refuel a gasoline-powered generator away from any flame or heat source. Be sure the generator is cool before refueling, because heat from the engine can ignite vapours.

There are people who, in a crisis, act on impulse and put themselves and often others at unnecessary risk. A classic example would be a fully clothed person who leaps into a swollen river to rescue someone, fails in the attempt, and drowns. A smarter-thinking person might have affected a rescue differently — perhaps by removing shoes and heavy clothing before diving in — and lived.

Avoid exposing yourself and others to undue danger, especially while undertaking rescue work in damaged buildings. Becoming a victim unnecessarily is as stupid an act as anyone can hope to commit at a time when every fully-functioning person is in high demand.

PEOPLE HAZARDS

The energy released by the January 26, 2001 Gujarat earthquake in western India, measuring 7.9 on the Richter scale, released 30,000 times more energy than the atomic bombs dropped over Japan during the Second World War. It was felt as far away as Bangladesh, 1,900 kilometres (1,180 miles) to the east astride the Bay of Bengal — the distance from Vancouver to Winnipeg or Los Angeles.

The following item appeared in *The Vancouver Sun* of June 30, 2000:

[Former Attorney-General Andrew] Petter was responding to a federal report made public Thursday that was critical of the province's emergency program....

The Provincial Emergency Program was criticized for being understaffed, poorly trained, confused and ill-equipped. But Petter said much has changed since the report was completed....

"No one should be complacent and assume that the government can do preparedness for them. Every individual needs to prepare themselves," Petter said. "That's the only way as a province that we'll be ready."[26]

Your first responsibility is to be prepared yourself, and this guide will get you there faster and more thoroughly than anything else. On your way to full personal preparedness, however, you would be wise to consider the slightly wider picture — the preparedness (or lack of preparedness) of your immediate neighbourhood, and the part that you might play in helping your neighbourhood to get its emergency preparedness act together. In the aftermath of a great quake (or any comparable disaster) you will be far better off with well-informed, well-prepared neighbours than with hopelessly ill-prepared ones.

Unless you live in an exceptionally cohesive, farsighted neighbourhood, most of your neighbours are, unfortunately, ill-prepared — too preoccupied with the minutiae and challenges of daily living to think about preparing for a disaster that, as they see it, may never happen and that, if it does, may not be all that serious.

For neighbourhood emergency preparedness to become a reality for them and you, it will probably be because you and a handful of others take the lead.

GOVERNMENT PROGRAMS

BC's Provincial Emergency Program (PEP), in partnership with the Justice Institute of British Columbia, BC Gas Utility, and the GVRD has developed a neighbourhood emergency preparedness program for BC communities. It offers courses in personal preparedness and trains neighbourhood teams to respond safely and effectively during a disaster.

> Although there is nothing that can be done to prevent a disaster such as an earthquake or flood, families can be prepared before a disaster strikes to cope effectively during the event and recover quickly after it is over. The degree to which our next emergency or disaster can be effectively handled in a neighbourhood is directly related to how well families and neighbours in that neighbourhood have prepared for it…. A team of neighbours with a variety of skills will have a much greater chance of survival following a disaster than individuals coping on their own. Working together according to a pre-arranged plan will likely speed up recovery as well.
>
> Neighbourhood Emergency Preparedness Program

It is a great concept, and I would like to be able to tell you that it is working well, but I can't. Courses along these lines have been presented for a number of years, but they are not widely available and their quality varies greatly.

North and West Vancouver, for example, are shining examples of municipal initiative, but they have reverted to their staple of offering personal preparedness courses with further courses — in utilities and fire suppression, light search and rescue, shelter and caregiving, damage assessment, etc. — being available only if a group requests them. Few such requests are received. One reason (apart from public apathy) is that course participants come from all over the North Shore and farther afield and are not usually immediate neighbours. They tend to disperse into the crisp night air at the end of the course, knowing little more about the person they sat next to than their first name — with no plans to come together as a team.

Wherever you live, call City Hall (or your local equivalent) or the fire department and ask for the emergency program co-ordinator. Find out what is available beyond personal emergency preparedness courses. If what's available looks worth participating in, go for it. If not, consider what follows.

TAKING A LEAD

In the absence of a viable neighbourhood emergency preparedness program in your area, you might want to initiate your own — for your immediate neighbourhood. For this to happen, you will need neighbours — just some — who are willing to take the threat of a major earthquake seriously.

That is where this book comes in. An earthquake big enough to rattle people's teeth without actually collapsing their homes would do it, or the government's spending heavily on a tell-it-like-it-really-is media campaign rather than a few thousand dollars on leaflets and advertising, but the next best alternative may be this guide. If someone can't get the point by reading the back cover, they won't have to delve far inside to hit alarming facts and encouraging answers. And if, having done that, they can't get the point, they will probably be beyond your ability to help.

THE PREPP INITIATIVE

This initiative is new and very grass-roots. How far it will go in assisting neighbourhoods towards reasonable preparedness is something that we will all have a chance to see. It will only go somewhere if people make the initiative their own. It may be the difference between your neighbourhood becoming prepared and not being prepared.

PREPP, by the way, is the acronym for the company formed to publish and market this guide — Pacific Rim Earthquake Preparedness Program Ltd — the wider purpose of which is to provide education and training in earthquake and emergency preparedness.

The PREPP Initiative involves getting this guide into the hands of as many neighbours as possible (as a "wake-up" call and their best possible route to personal preparedness); providing those who are interested with the opportunity to form an emergency response team; and then facilitating that process. It's as simple as that.

Your starting point is to become familiar with this guide — especially with passages that highlight the threat and offer solutions. Then introduce this guide and the subject of emergency preparedness to one or more of your more approachable neighbours, ones living on your block, or back-to-back with your block, or within three or four minutes walk of your home if you live on a street — and enlist their support.

    You may want the support of a friend living in another neighbourhood, and in due course help him or her in the same way.

STEP 1

With or without help, you are going to have to introduce this guide to others — unless you can think of a better way of easing them or jolting them out of their complacency with regard to the Big One.

    One way would be to drop by neighbours, those you know and those you don't, inviting them to the home party "launch" of this guide that you will be holding shortly. Let them know that copies of the guide will be available at a discount of your choice. If you live in Greater Vancouver, you may be able to throw in that the author will be there to sign copies. Hand everyone a printed slip with the launch details on it. *(You can call us at PREPP for a single-page flyer to which you can add your own information.)*

    Another way would be for you and one or more buddies to take copies of this guide directly to your neighbours — knocking on their doors exactly as you would if you were looking for your lost anaconda or canvassing for a marked crossing at the end of the street. Show them a copy of this guide, tell them how useful you are finding it, and explain that you can sell it to them for up to 25 per cent off the cover price (your choice). Whether they buy or not, hand them a flyer inviting them to the meeting that you will be holding to look at the formation of an informal neighbourhood emergency response team. *(You can obtain a sample flyer from us, ready to complete with your details and copy.)*

    Where will the books come from? You can order them from us on a "sale or return" basis. We will sell them to you at our regular discounts, starting at 25 per cent *(see order form on page 277)*, with a further 10 per cent rebate and a refund of the shipping charge if a viable neighbourhood team gets formed as a result of this initiative.

    You may, of course, be able to improve on these suggestions, in which case please let us know so that we can pass good ideas on to others via our website, *www.earthquakeprep.ca.* You might, for example, want to work through your Block Watch, yoga class, dance club, church,

STEP 2

or any other entity that already has neighbours and others associating and co-operating with each other. Whatever you do, make this guide available, either directly or by letting people know how they can buy it from us. And bear in mind the potential of this guide as a fundraiser and means of spreading the word.

STEP 3   The purpose of your first, exploratory meeting will be to seek agreement that personal preparedness is vital and that neighbours-helping-neighbours in a co-ordinated way in a crisis is what you would like to make possible. Discuss this, giving everyone present the opportunity to voice their thoughts, but keep it brief. The main things you need to know at this stage are who's on board and what skills, equipment, and facilities, if any, they might bring to the group.

STEP 4   This step we can look at when you get there. It will be the process by which your group develops into a useful task force. The help you need will be there. Be in touch with us at PREPP and we will point you in whatever directions are right for you and send you briefing materials. Depending on where you're located, we can arrange for training sessions if these are not readily available from your local authorities. But steps 1 through 3 need to be accomplished first.

WORST CASE SCENARIO   This initiative may not work for you — or you may not work for it — in which case you will give your surplus copies away as gifts, or return them to us in mint condition for a full refund of the book price. You will, meanwhile, have met and related to neighbours in a creative way and planted valuable seeds. It's as risk-free as that. More likely, you will be calling to ask us for additional copies and for help with Step 4, and we will be keeping your team and others informed and in touch via our website, *www.earthquakeprep.ca*.

EMERGENCY SOCIAL SERVICES   There's a bigger picture than your immediate neighbourhood. If you are willing to volunteer for service to the wider community in a disaster, the Emergency Social Services (ESS) program is the route to follow. This province-wide network is made up of thousands of dedicated, trained individuals, including members of The Salvation Army, the Canadian Red Cross, St John Ambulance, and other organizations. These are the front line volunteers who, for example, set up and staff reception centres and emergency shelters in a disaster. Following a major earthquake, these will be established in whatever suitable buildings are still standing — recreation centres, school gymnasiums, church halls, hotel conference and meeting rooms, and shopping malls — or in tents and trailers in municipal parks, campgrounds, school playing fields, and parking lots.

As best they can, these people will provide emergency food, clothing, and shelter services; register evacuees, take inquiries about people's safety and whereabouts and assist in reuniting families; provide accurate and up-to-date information on the current situation; provide basic first aid; assist with public health issues such as safe water, food, and sanitation; train the numerous "walk-in" volunteers eager to help in co-ordinated ways; provide assistance to people with special needs, including children separated from their parents, the dependent elderly, people with language difficulties, and people with physical or mental disabilities; assist with the care of domestic pets; and provide emotional support for evacuees and response workers.

The ESS program is well organized. Their training is free and the services that they provide in times of crisis are invaluable. To find out more, call the Emergency Social Services Association *(see below)*.

Resources that you may find useful include:

USEFUL CONTACTS

- **Emergency Social Services Association (ESSA)**
  Tel: 604 517-1442 or 1-800 910-ESSA toll free
  www.essa.bc.ca
  A non-profit association established to support the more than 5,500 ESS volunteers in BC in the development and maintenance of their emergency social services programs.

- **Provincial Emergency Program (PEP)**
  Tel: 250 952-4913
  www.pep.bc.ca
  Their mandate is to maintain effective awareness, preparation, response, and recovery programs to reduce the human and financial costs of emergencies and disasters.

- **Canadian Red Cross Society**
  Tel: 604 709-6600 or 1-800 565-8000 toll free
  www.redcross.ca

- **St John Ambulance**
  Tel: 604 321-2652
  Course information and registration: 604 321-2651
  (or look in your *SuperPages*)
  www.sja.ca

- **The Salvation Army in BC**
  Tel: 604 299-3908
  Emergency Disaster Services: 604 296-3822
  (or look in your *SuperPages*)
  www.sallyann.org

- **Office of Critical Infrastructure Protection and Emergency Preparedness**
  Tel: 250 363-3621
  www.ocipep.gc.ca
  A civilian organization operating within the Department of National Defence. They are the government's primary agency for ensuring national civil emergency preparedness for all types of emergencies.

- **E-Comm Centre**
  Tel: 604 215-5000
  www.ecomm.bc.ca
  E-Comm Emergency Communications is a recently formed corporation that serves as the consolidated centre for emergency communications in southwestern British Columbia. The corporation is housed in a state-of-the-art, post-disaster building that will survive through an emergency situation in order to facilitate all aspects of public safety.

COMMUNITY INVOLVEMENT CHECKLIST

GOVERNMENT WORKSHOPS

You have investigated what is available ☐

You and others in your household have taken one or more of these workshops ☐

THE PREPP INITIATIVE

Step 1: You are familiar with this guide and have introduced it to one or more immediate neighbours and/or friends ☐

Step 2: You have started into the home party "launch" or canvassing process, or are spreading the word in other ways ☐

Step 3: You have held your first neighbourhood emergency response team meeting and are poised for Step 4 — the building of a team ☐

EMERGENCY SOCIAL SERVICES

You have approached ESSA with a view to becoming a volunteer ☐

Section 30
RESOURCES

H ERE ARE A COUPLE OF VIDEOS AND
three books that will fill out and round out the information in this guide.

- ***The San Francisco Earthquake! October 17, 1989***
An MPI Home Video presentation of an ABC News production. A vivid account of the 1989 Bay Area quake and its aftermath. Running time: approx. 60 minutes.

  Available from Library Video Company, PO Box 580, Wynnewood, PA 19096, USA, telephone 610 645-4000 or
1-800 843-3620, price $14.95 US plus $7.50 shipping.

- ***Is Your Home Earthquake Resistant? Improve Your Odds in the Big One!***
Presented by the Provincial Emergency Program (PEP) and Canada Mortgage & Housing Corporation (CMHC). Exceptionally clear explanations concerning the upgrading of your home, including ensuring that your home is bolted to its foundations, reinforcing sheer walls, and protecting yourself from the hazards of tumbling chimney bricks, hot water tanks, refrigerators, and other heavy objects. Clear demonstrations of how upgrades should be carried out. Running time: approx. 25 minutes.

  Available from CMHC, 200-1111 West Georgia Street, Vancouver BC V6E 4S4, telephone 604 731-5733, price $19.95 Cdn, plus shipping and GST.

The first of these titles is an authoritative guide to preparing one's home. The second takes a very readable look at earthquakes and volcanoes as worldwide phenomena with which many of us must live. And the third paints a vivid picture of the huge earthquake for which Tokyo — rather like Greater Vancouver and Victoria — is imminently due and inadequately prepared. That picture, as the book states,

> sounds like fiction, and that is the problem. Though this nightmare scenario has already been accepted and laid out in several national and local government studies as the consequence of another 1923-type earthquake, it is so horrendous and catastrophic, people simply refuse to accept it.[27]

You should be able to obtain these books through your public library:

- ***Residential Guide to Earthquake Resistance***

  Produced by Canada Mortgage & Housing Corporation (CMHC), 338 pages.

  This well-illustrated manual takes you through the step-by-step process of securing a home against earthquake damage. There is a wealth of information in it for experts and for the layperson wanting to know what needs to be done and how it should be done.

  Available from CMHC, 200-1111 West Georgia Street, Vancouver BC V6E 4S4, Canada, telephone 604 731-5733. Price: $39.95 Cdn, plus shipping and GST.

- ***The Earth in Turmoil: Earthquakes, Volcanoes, and their Impact on Humankind***

  Sieh, Kerry and LeVay, Simon, New York: W. H. Freeman & Company, 324 pages, 1998.

  You will find quotes from this highly readable book in the Overview of this guide and in *Section 32, Endnotes* — examples of the authors' fascinating and frequently anecdotal accounts of seismic and volcanic activity around the world.

  Available in bookstores. Price: $23.95 Cdn ($14.95 US)

- ***Sixty Seconds that will Change the World: The Coming Tokyo Earthquake***

  Hadfield, Peter, Boston MA: Tuttle Publishing, 209 pages, 1991.

  Peter Hadfield, a freelance journalist, has for a long time been a correspondent for the Canadian Broadcasting Corporation in Japan.

  Out of print: unavailable in bookstores, but available through on-line marketplaces (search under used or secondhand books).

  This unusual, compelling book describes the vulnerability of present-day Tokyo (one of the largest cities on earth and the hub of the entire Japanese economy) to the devastating earthquake that it can expect at any time. It predicts the cataclysmic human and economic consequences of such a quake.

  In the opening chapter, the author describes the Great Kanto Earthquake of September 1, 1923 and its fiery aftermath, in which 142,000 people died. Here is an excerpt:

  One of the biggest problems was disposing of the thousands of bodies that littered the streets and choked the waterways. The Sumida was full of bloated and discoloured corpses, which were pulled out and burned as quickly as possible. Others were piled high in the streets where they lay, and cremated. The gruesome business of collecting bodies continued for days and revealed the horrifying circumstances of some of the deaths. Hundreds suffocated in a crush at Hongo station, where crowds had gathered to escape the flames. Many more were found floating in the ponds of Yoshiwara and Asakusa and the canals of the Honjo. They had not drowned and neither had they succumbed to the flames. They had simply been boiled alive.

Others were found on pavements — dead yet unburnt. They had suffocated in the smoke, but the reason for this became horribly clear on further examination. During the conflagration, tarmac on the pavements became so hot it melted. Those who suffocated had been fleeing from the fire when they became stuck, literally, in the melting tarmac and unable to move.[28]

But that was eight decades ago, you might say: you're scare-mongering us! That's right. If our Big One is only one tenth as awful as the one described above, you will be exceedingly glad to have taken adequate precautions ahead of time. Some things don't change much and the horrors of a giant earthquake is one of them.

Here is a small part of what Peter Hadfield had to say about the recent Kobe earthquake:

When a major earthquake hit Kobe in early January 1995, thousands of people were left to die beneath the rubble as the rescue operation turned into disorganized chaos.

There has always been a complacency bordering on arrogance among city planners and government officials here [in Tokyo, Japan].... What I found was that the preparations and plans were inadequate and the codes frequently ignored. Rescue crews who trained to perfection under ideal conditions had little idea of what a real disaster would look like.

The Kobe disaster exposed those inadequacies. As expected, roads were blocked and impassable and fire trucks couldn't move into the most heavily damaged areas. Water pipes broke and fires were left to burn out of control for lack of water to tackle them.[29]

Are we any better prepared than Kobe was? It would be nice to think so. In our case, complacency is probably far more ascribable to us, the inhabitants of southwestern British Columbia, than to our planners and government officials, who are taking precautions despite our indifference.

WEBSITE Your main reason for visiting our website, *www.earthquakeprep.ca*, will likely be for its Resources and Updates/Fresh Ideas sections, in which you will find referrals to reliable suppliers of items and services recommended in the guide, input from fellow readers, and fresh information from other sources.

Anyone whose introduction to this book is through our website will find:

- **a preview, including:**
  - **the cover**
  - **the contents page**
  - **the Overview and Preparation sections**
  - **an author profile**

- **earthquake facts, including:**
  - **the threat facing British Columbia and the United States Pacific Northwest**
  - **the Richter scale**
  - **historical earthquakes**

- **FAQs — answers to frequently asked questions**

- **testimonials**

- **updates and fresh ideas**

- **a resources section**

- **ordering information**

- **contact information**

- **and a whole lot more....**

P REPP IS THE ACRONYM FOR THE
company formed to publish and market this guide and provide
education and training in earthquake and emergency preparedness —
Pacific Rim Earthquake Preparedness Program Ltd.

FEEDBACK

The author and publishers would appreciate receiving any input that
will help improve future editions. Your comments, ideas, suggestions,
recommendations, and helpful advice will be very welcome. If you have
anything to contribute, please write, call, fax, or e-mail Graem Castell at:

Pacific Rim Earthquake Preparedness Program Ltd (or PREPP)
PO Box 29193
1950 West Broadway
Vancouver BC V6J 5C2

Telephone: 604 733-4033 or
1-800 733-4070 toll free (Canada and US)
Fax: 604 731-5435
E-mail: info@earthquakeprep.ca

Please let us have your name, address, telephone number, and
e-mail address so that we can be in touch with you, if necessary.

ORDERING THIS GUIDE

The cover price of this guide is $29.95 Cdn/$21.95 US. You can order
copies directly from us at discounts starting at 25 per cent off the cover
price — as outlined on the order form on page 277.

Orders of 500 or more copies of this guide can be supplied as
Special Editions. These come with an attractive, semi-transparent first
page with whatever information the company or organization would
like on it — for example, the corporate name and logo, a message from
the president or CEO, and one or more photographs or other images.
These editions are designed to be used as gifts for employees,
customers, clients, suppliers, advisers, and others — or for resale. They
also make great fundraisers.

- **telephone orders**
  Call 604 216-8008 or 1-800 338-3320 toll free (Canada and US) for our
  24-hour answering service. Have your VISA or MasterCard ready
  and follow the simple instructions.

- **fax orders**
  Photocopy the order form opposite, complete it, and fax it to us at 604 731-5435, including your VISA or MasterCard number and expiry date.

- **mail orders**
  Photocopy the order form opposite, complete it, and mail it to us at the address above with your VISA or MasterCard number and expiry date, corporate cheque, or money order, payable to PREPP.

- **corporate orders**
  Please include a purchase order number, if applicable.

PRESENTATIONS AND WORKSHOPS

The author is available to give presentations based on the contents of this book, and PREPP will be pleased to recommend experienced workshop and course leaders for whatever aspects of earthquake and emergency preparedness may be relevant to you, including:

- **Basic Emergency Preparedness for Home and Workplace** (50 minutes to 3 hours)

- **Workplace Emergency Response Team (ERT) Training** (Basic level, 6 1/2 hours; Advanced level, which includes Basic, 13 hours; Core Team, 6 1/2 hours)

- **Triage (Disaster First Aid)** (4 hours)

- **Rapid Damage Assessment** (Basic, 4 hours: Advanced, for which Basic is not a pre-requisite, 8 hours)

- **Light Urban Search and Rescue** (8 hours)

- **Fire Emergency Supervisory Staff (Fire Warden)** (Basic, 4 hours)

- **Fire Extinguisher** (2 1/2 hours)

- **All levels of Canadian Red Cross, EMP Canada, and WCB first aid programs**

All of these courses and seminars are customized to clients' needs and take into consideration previous experience, the numbers involved, resources, and the workplace environment and associated hazards.

ORDER FORM

COVER PRICE
$29.95 Cdn / $21.95 US

DIRECT ORDER DISCOUNTS: Approx

1-9 copies $22.50 Cdn / $16.45 US   25% off

10-24 copies $20.95 Cdn / $15.35 US   30% off

25-49 copies $19.45 Cdn / $14.25 US   35% off

50-99 copies $17.95 Cdn / $13.15 US   40% off

For 100 copies or more, call for a quotation

- **CALL** 604 216-8008 or 1-800 338-3320 toll free in Canada and US (24-hour answering) (have your VISA or MasterCard ready)
- **FAX** a completed photocopy of this form to 604 731-5435
- **MAIL** a completed photocopy of this form with money order, corporate cheque, or VISA or MasterCard details to PREPP, PO Box 29193, 1950 West Broadway, Vancouver, BC V6J 5C2, Canada

CANADIAN ORDERS
(For shipment within Canada – Canadian funds)

_____ copies @ $ _____ Cdn $_____

Shipping (1st book) $ __6.50__
Add $3.50 shipping for
each additional book* $_____

GST (7%) $_____

TOTAL $_____

US ORDERS
(For shipment to the USA – US funds)

_____ copies @ $ _____ US $_____

Shipping (1st book) $ __8.00__

Add $4.00 shipping for
each additional book* $_____

TOTAL $_____

OVERSEAS ORDERS
(Outside Canada and the USA – US funds)

_____ copies @ $ _____ US $_____

Shipping** (1st book) $ __8.00__

Add $4.00 shipping for
each additional book* $_____

TOTAL $_____

* For shipping over 10 books, please call for a quotation.   ** Surface mail — for airmail or Xpress, please contact us for a quotation.

METHOD OF PAYMENT   please print clearly

VISA ☐   MasterCard ☐   Card number: _____   Expiry: _____

Name on card: _____   Cardholder's signature: _____

Money order ☐   or Corporate cheque ☐   payable to PREPP   Corporate orders, please add purchase order # _____

ORDERED BY: _____

Company: _____

Address: _____

City Prov/State: _____

P/Zip Code: _____ Country: _____

E-mail address: _____

Day telephone: (_____) _____

SHIP TO: _____

Company: _____

Address: _____

City Prov/State: _____

P/Zip Code: _____ Country: _____

E-mail address: _____

Day telephone: (_____) _____

IMPORTANT TO US – How did you first hear about this guide?

☐ Radio ad   ☐ Vehicle ad   ☐ Friend/Colleague   ☐ Fax broadcast   ☐ Other

☐ Newspaper ad   ☐ Website   ☐ Door-to-door sales   ☐ E-mail broadcast   Describe _____

Pacific Rim Earthquake Preparedness Program Ltd
PO Box 29193, 1950 West Broadway, Vancouver, BC V6J 5C2, Canada
Telephone 604 733-4033 or 1-800 733-4070 toll free (Canada and US) Fax 604 731-5435
E-mail: info@earthquakeprep.ca Website: www.earthquakeprep.ca

ANOTHER HOUSEHOLD ON ITS WAY TO BEING PREPARED

The following excerpts are from an article in *The Province* of April 20, 2001:

Silent 'quake' could trigger the Big One

In August 1999, the small Vancouver Island fishing village of Ucluelet switched directions. The village — and most of the island — moves east toward Vancouver by about 15 millimetres each year. But for a month, it headed southwest.

Scientists from Natural Resources Canada have discovered that's because of a "slip" beneath the Cascadia fault. Their findings, published yesterday in the journal *Science*, are the first to show such a slip in North America, although one has been documented in Japan and there is evidence that a major earthquake in Chile in 1960 was caused by one.

The August 1999 slip was a rupture equivalent to an earthquake of 6.7, about the same magnitude as the one that rattled Seattle and Vancouver in February, causing significant damage in Seattle. And while the slips aren't noticeable because they happen so slowly, they may play a role in building up pressure on the fault, write scientists.

"It is conceivable that one of these slip events may... evolve into a trigger mechanism for a great subduction thrust earthquake," wrote scientists Herb Dragert, Kelin Wang and Thomas James, of the Pacific Geoscience Centre in Sidney. Translation: the Big One, a devastating quake about eight or nine in magnitude that scientists say could hit the Pacific coast at any time....

What happened in 1999 between August 18 and September 29 was an earthquake without the quake. The slow movement took place along the part of the fault so deep beneath the Earth's surface that the hot, plastic crust of the Juan de Fuca plate could slip easily under the North American plate.

If the movement had occurred closer to the Earth's surface, where the plates are rough, it would have caused the friction that produces earthquakes.

It's only recently that technology has advanced enough to allow scientists to detect this kind of slide. By studying data beamed from satellites, scientists know western North America is being pulled east as the oceanic Juan de Fuca plate pushes underneath the North American plate. Dragert noticed that for that period in 1999, there was a shift in direction.

James said: "It started in the south of Puget Sound and southern Vancouver Island and it travelled to the southwest over a period of about 35 days. We think these kinds of events occur every few years, perhaps as frequently as once every year or two."

Scientists believe that there was a similar movement just before the 1960 Chile quake that may have sped up and become the earthquake itself....

James said megathrust earthquakes happen on average about every five hundred years, but they can occur as frequently as every 200 years or as far apart as 700 years. The last megaquake along the Pacific coast happened in January 1700 — 301 years ago — according to written records from Japan....[30]

1. Sieh, Kerry and LeVay, Simon, *The Earth in Turmoil: Earthquakes, Volcanoes, and their Impact on Humankind,* New York: W. H. Freeman and Company, 1998, p.25.

A curious circumstance has allowed this most recent earthquake to be dated to the precise year, date, and even time of day. In 1994, Kenji Satake, a seismologist with the Geological Survey of Japan, attended a paleoseismology workshop in California at which the history of subduction earthquakes in the Pacific Northwest was discussed. He knew that large subduction earthquakes can cause tsunamis that cross the Pacific Ocean. Therefore, when he returned home, Satake and his colleagues combed through old tsunami records covering the period around 300 years ago. They found several documents that mentioned a tsunami that came ashore in Honshu in January 1700. By carefully eliminating all other potential sources, they concluded that this tsunami was probably caused by a rupture of the Cascadia subduction zone. Knowing the speed at which tsunamis travel across the ocean, Satake and his colleagues were able to fix the time of the earthquake at about nine in the evening, local time, on January 26, 1700. And on the basis of the size of the tsunami, they were able to estimate the size of the earthquake: it has a magnitude of about 9.0 — in the same size range, in other words, as the giant Chilean earthquake of 1960 [magnitude 9.5] and the Alaskan earthquake of 1964 [magnitude 9.2].

A final piece of evidence clinches the story. Having heard of Satake's work, Atwater went back to his dead red cedar trees on the Copalis River. Although the outermost rings on the trees' trunks had weathered away, the rings in some of the submerged roots were fully preserved. Dating root rings is notoriously difficult, but by tracing individual rings in the roots up into the trees' trunk, where they could be dated, Atwater was able to establish the year of the trees' final growing season: it was 1699.

According to the US Geological Survey's Circular 1187, Japanese government records of 1700 confirm that in Miyako, on the northeast coast of Honshu,

people went to high ground to escape the [Cascadia tsunami which] destroyed 13 houses, set off a fire that burned 20 more, and caused authorities to issue rice to 159 people.

2. Sieh, LeVay, 1998, p.25.

[It is estimated that] there have been at least 12 giant earthquakes on the Cascadia subduction zone over the past 7,700 years.

Stay tuned for the Big One, A3, Craig McInnes, *The Vancouver Sun*, March 1, 2001.

There have been 13 megathrust quakes [in the Cascadia subduction zone] over the last 6,000 years.

3. *There's Real Reason To Quake — Expert*, A1, Margaret Munro, *The Vancouver Sun*, January 5, 1994.)

If you didn't believe them before, BC's top earthquake scientists say, you should believe them now. Southwestern British Columbia is in for a massive earthquake.

A comprehensive study [headed by Garry Rogers, head of earthquake studies at the federal Pacific Geoscience Centre outside Victoria]... says the tectonic plates west of Vancouver Island are locked and storing pressure... in a zone about 70 kilometres wide, [the inner edge of which] is about 30 kilometres beneath the outer edge of Vancouver Island.

The lead author of the new study, Herb Dragert, has found that mountains on Vancouver Island and on the Canadian and US sides of the Strait of Juan de Fuca are moving steadily northeastward at up to several centimetres a year. The movement attests to forces building 20 to 80 kilometres beneath the surface. The scientists have found that Vancouver Island is tipping slowly toward the east as the underground pressure builds....

If the Juan de Fuca plate jarred free tomorrow... it would slip about 13.5 metres and generate a tsunami measuring about five metres high. It would hit communities along the outer coast of Vancouver Island within minutes.... The quake would send out seismic waves that could cause extensive damage throughout southwestern BC.... "The total effect could be catastrophic."

4. *The World Book Encyclopedia,* Chicago, London, Sydney, Toronto: World Book Inc, 1997, P/Volume15, p.561.

5. Ibid.

6. David Gronbeck-Jones, Emergency Management Analyst (Earthquakes) at the Victoria headquarters of the Provincial Emergency Program, in a letter to the author.

Off the west coast of Vancouver Island... several tectonic plates come together. In one large region known as the Cascadia subduction zone, extending from about the middle of Vancouver Island all the way to Northern California, the plates appear to be locked. No significant earthquakes have happened there for some time. Strain forces are building in this region, causing measurable deformation of the earth's crust up to several hundred kilometres away. When the strain becomes too great, the locked plates will move and a very large earthquake, or even a series of large earthquakes, will occur.

7. Sieh, LeVay, 1998, pp.26-27 and p.293.

8. Sieh, LeVay, 1998, p.18.
   When the subduction zone off southern Chile slipped in 1960, it unleashed the biggest earthquake ever recorded — a behemoth that not only devastated 600 miles of Chilean coastline but also sent tsunamis across the Pacific, drowning hundreds of people in Hawaii and Japan. A total of about 5,700 people died. The earthquake earned a 9.5 on the moment magnitude earthquake scale.

9. *Are You Ready For The Big One?*, F4, Michael Kane, *The Vancouver Sun*, February 18, 2000.

10. *Water Treatment Devices for Disinfection of Drinking Water*, Health Canada, June 5, 2000.

11. *Compendium of Pharmaceuticals and Specialties*, Canadian Pharmacists Association, 2000.

12. Ibid.

13. Ibid.

14. Ibid.

15. *You call that an earthquake?*, B3, Stephen Hume, *The Vancouver Sun*, March 5, 2001.

16. Ibid.

17. Ibid.

18. Reproduced with the kind permission of the author.

19. Yanev, Peter I., *Peace of Mind in Earthquake Country*, San Francisco, CA: Chronicle Books, 1991.

20. *The Big One*, A10 and A12, *The Province*, July 23-24, 2000.

21. *Another Quake, Another Reminder*, D4, Stephen Hume, *The Vancouver Sun*, June 6, 1998.

22. *The Big One*, A10 and A12, *The Province*, July 23-24, 2000.

23. Ibid.

24. *BC quake study heightens fear of Big One*, Metro A1, Robert Matas, *The Globe and Mail*, April 20, 2001.

25. Hadfield, Peter, *Sixty Seconds that will Change the World: The Coming Tokyo Earthquake*, Boston MA: Tuttle Publishing, 1991, p.184.

26. *Earthquake Response Adequate*, B5, Jim Beatty, *The Vancouver Sun*, June 30, 2000.

27. Hadfield, Peter, *Sixty Seconds that will Change the World: The Coming Tokyo Earthquake*, Boston MA: Tuttle Publishing, 1991, p.89.

28. Hadfield, 1991, pp.9-10.

29. Hadfield, 1991, pp.xiii-xiv.

30. *Silent "quake" could trigger the Big One*, A3, Canadian Press, *The Province*, April 20, 2001.

Section 33
INDEX

ORDER FORM

COVER PRICE
$29.95 Cdn / $21.95 US

DIRECT ORDER DISCOUNTS:

		Approx
1-9 copies	$22.50 Cdn / $16.45 US	25% off
10-24 copies	$20.95 Cdn / $15.35 US	30% off
25-49 copies	$19.45 Cdn / $14.25 US	35% off
50-99 copies	$17.95 Cdn / $13.15 US	40% off

For 100 copies or more, call for a quotation

- **CALL** 604 216-8008 or 1-800 338-3320 toll free in Canada and US (24-hour answering) (have your VISA or MasterCard ready)
- **FAX** a completed photocopy of this form to 604 731-5435
- **MAIL** a completed photocopy of this form with money order, corporate cheque, or VISA or MasterCard details to PREPP, PO Box 29193, 1950 West Broadway, Vancouver, BC V6J 5C2, Canada

CANADIAN ORDERS
(For shipment within Canada – Canadian funds)

____ copies @ $ _____ Cdn $_____

Shipping (1st book) $__6.50__
Add $3.50 shipping for
each additional book* $_____

GST (7%) $_____

TOTAL $_____

US ORDERS
(For shipment to the USA – US funds)

____ copies @ $ _____ US $_____

Shipping (1st book) $__8.00__

Add $4.00 shipping for
each additional book* $_____

TOTAL $_____

OVERSEAS ORDERS
(Outside Canada and the USA – US funds)

____ copies @ $ _____ US $_____

Shipping** (1st book) $__8.00__

Add $4.00 shipping for
each additional book* $_____

TOTAL $_____

* For shipping over 10 books, please call for a quotation. ** Surface mail — for airmail or Xpress, please contact us for a quotation.

METHOD OF PAYMENT please print clearly

VISA ☐ MasterCard ☐ Card number: _____ Expiry: _____

Name on card: _____ Cardholder's signature: _____

Money order ☐ or Corporate cheque ☐ payable to PREPP Corporate orders, please add purchase order # _____

ORDERED BY: _____

Company: _____

Address: _____

City Prov/State: _____

P/Zip Code: _____ Country: _____

E-mail address: _____

Day telephone: (_____) _____

SHIP TO: _____

Company: _____

Address: _____

City Prov/State: _____

P/Zip Code: _____ Country: _____

E-mail address: _____

Day telephone: (_____) _____

IMPORTANT TO US – How did you first hear about this guide?

☐ Radio ad ☐ Vehicle ad ☐ Friend/Colleague ☐ Fax broadcast ☐ Other

☐ Newspaper ad ☐ Website ☐ Door-to-door sales ☐ E-mail broadcast Describe _____

Pacific Rim Earthquake Preparedness Program Ltd
PO Box 29193, 1950 West Broadway, Vancouver, BC V6J 5C2, Canada
Telephone 604 733-4033 or 1-800 733-4070 toll free (Canada and US) Fax 604 731-5435
E-mail: info@earthquakeprep.ca Website: www.earthquakeprep.ca

EARTHQUAKE!
Preparing for the Big One
BRITISH COLUMBIA
by
Graem Castell

If you live in southwestern British Columbia or the Pacific Northwest of the United States, you live in earthquake country. It may not seem that way, because recent earthquakes here have been relatively minor — large enough to cause a stir and small enough to convince us that earthquakes are no big deal.

Every two to eight hundred years, however, for thousands of years, this region has suffered a truly gigantic earthquake — far larger than most of us can imagine. The last one was on January 26, 1700. With an estimated magnitude of about 9.0, it was over a hundred times more severe and a thousand times more powerful than the 6.8 quake of February 28, 2001, centred near Olympia, Washington. The resulting tsunami wreaked havoc on the coast of Japan, 7,600 kilometres (4,700 miles) away.

There were few people living here at the time — just a few First Nations settlements in a wilderness of trees. The effect of such an earthquake now would be immense, and such a quake is due. It is inevitable — it will happen. The only questions are how soon and how powerful it will be. Its effects on most of our lives will be devastating.

This guide makes preparing for the Big One (or any comparable disaster) as easy and effective as it is ever going to get. Using it will greatly increase anyone's chances of emerging from this catastrophe relatively unscathed — possibly, even, with flying colours.

THE DEFINITIVE GUIDE
FILLED WITH CHECKLISTS
HANDS-ON
HIGHLY EFFECTIVE